13-7

Yours respectfully

Theobald Boehm.

Munich the 4th of March 1872.

THE FLUTE AND FLUTE-PLAYING

IN ACOUSTICAL, TECHNICAL, AND ARTISTIC ASPECTS

by
THEOBALD BOEHM
Royal Bavarian Court-Musician

Translated by
DAYTON C. MILLER
With a new introduction by
SAMUEL BARON
*Flutist, New York Woodwind Quintet and
New York Chamber Soloists*

NEW YORK
DOVER PUBLICATIONS, INC.

ABIGAIL E. WEEKS MEMORIAL LIBRARY
UNION COLLEGE
BARBOURVILLE, KENTUCKY

788.51
B676

Copyright © 1964 by Dover Publications, Inc.
All rights reserved under Pan American and International Copyright Conventions.

This Dover edition, first published in 1964, is an unabridged and unaltered republication of the second revised and enlarged edition published by Dayton C. Miller in 1922.

This Dover edition also contains a new Introduction by Samuel Baron.

Library of Congress Catalog Card Number: 64-15498

Manufactured in the United States of America

Dover Publications, Inc.
180 Varick Street
New York 14, N.Y.

PREFACE TO THE DOVER EDITION

Theobald Boehm had a unique combination of skills. He was a master flutist, a master gold- and silversmith, and a keen student of physics and acoustics as they apply to the flute. The master flutist and musician realized what was lacking in the flute of his day: his ear was dissatisfied with the poor intonation, limited range and uneven tonal response of his chosen instrument. The keen student of physics and acoustics considered what might be the causes, what might be the improvements. And finally the mechanic, the man who could make things and make them work, created the forms that could realize his ideas.

All of this is known from history, and we flutists know it best of all, for we play on a Boehm flute virtually unchanged from his work bench of 1847 to the present day. There have been fine flute makers since, and many splendid flutes have been built, but the design, the proportions and the *theory* of the flute come from this book, which is as valid today as it ever was.

Reading Boehm's book is an absorbing experience in following the progress of an idea. But it is more than that, too. The view of the man himself is enlightening and endearing. He writes in a most objective style but he cannot conceal the mellowness of a hard-won wisdom. This wisdom is shared openly with all who are interested. It is the ideal attitude of the scientist who says, "We are all working to penetrate the unknown. My contribution may help someone else; it may throw some light on a seemingly unrelated problem; it may have an application that I don't think of.   Let anyone who is interested know my work!"

In addition there is an attitude about the old man that stamps him as a great teacher.   To Boehm, the creative man is the one who teaches *himself* something. It follows from this that he can teach others too. Notice the emphasis on the *rational* process and the *rational* ideal in the following words of Boehm:

> . . . for he alone is capable of carrying out a rational work, who can give a complete account of the why and wherefore of every detail from the conception to the completion. (*An Essay on the Construction of Flutes*)

This emphasis is carried through his work.

Boehm's respect for the practical and the pragmatic is very strong.   Again and again he finds the solution to his problem by trying many ways.   For example: how to determine the shortening of the tube necessary to give the chromatic intervals of the bottom octave. Boehm's solution:

> The simplest and shortest method is, naturally, successively to cut off from the lower end of the flute tube so much as will make the length of the air column correspond to each tone of the chromatic scale.   In order that these proportions might be accurately verified, I made a tube in which all the twelve tone sections could be taken off and again put together.   (*The Flute and Flute-Playing*, p. 25)

When he had accomplished this much he found that the placement of the tone holes did not exactly correspond to the cutting off of the tube, so he endeavored to find the relationship between the two systems:

> For the exact determination of these positions and the other tuning proportions, I had a flute made with movable holes, and was thus enabled to adjust all the tones higher or lower at pleasure.   (*The Flute and Flute-Playing*, p. 30)

At this point I ask the reader, just what is a flute with movable tone holes? To my unmechanical mind, such an ingenious gadget should win prizes for its inventor, but for Boehm it was merely a means to an end. It was a step along the way—he never mentions it again.

So we have here a very interesting man, one who had the patience and courage, not to mention the ingenuity, to see his work through "from the conception to the completion" even though he was going against the beliefs of his time. For in Boehm's day musicians and instrument makers believed that the holes should be bored into the flute at points where the player's fingers could easily cover them. This was considered to be common sense as well as "humanistic." Boehm said, in effect, "Let us put the holes where they belong, according to science and the tempered scale. If the fingers cannot reach them, let us use our brain to invent some system for controlling the opening and shutting of the tone holes." This was uncommon sense, and humanistic on a higher plane.

A flutist of international reputation, he did not hesitate, at the age of thirty-eight, to redesign his own instrument, endangering, as he says,

> ... my facility in playing which had been acquired by twenty years of practice. (*The Flute and Flute-Playing*, p. 3)

And when the new instrument was not completely satisfactory to him, he did not shrink from taking two years for the study of physics and acoustics (at the age of fifty-two) and utilizing what he then learned to make still more drastic revisions in his design. At no point did he allow himself to be swayed by the comments of his fellow professionals who might have said, "Look

here!   Aren't you really ruining the business for us?
Our students are going to take this new flute, as you
call it, and do better than we can—and we have given
our lives to the flute!"

All who are interested in the flute should visit the
Library of Congress in Washington, D.C., which
houses the flute collection of Dayton C. Miller, translator and editor of this book.   There on display are
many of the best flutes of pre-Boehm days.   What
monstrosities of frustrated ingenuity are to be seen
there!   One maker devised a Rube Goldberg key to
trill C♯ to D♯.   Another figured out three ways to
play F natural and built them all onto the instrument.
A hodge-podge of keys and levers seems to grow in
baroque profusion over the simple flute of Quantz—but
to little avail.   The instrument is still limited in range,
still out of tune, and clumsy to play in the remote keys.
By contrast, Boehm's flute, which put an end to this
"let's add a key here and another there" mentality—
how simple! how functional! how really well it plays!

How satisfying is the triumph of a rational work!

SAMUEL BARON

April, 1964.

Munich, August 6th, 1908

Dear Mr. Miller:—

I wish to express my, and my sister's, great pleasure and satisfaction for your labor of love, which you have undertaken in the good intention to honor my grandfather. For this we can be only very thankful to you; and I believe I express the sentiment of the whole family of my grandfather in giving you our approval of the publishing of your translation of his book: "Die Flöte und das Flötenspiel."

Yours very truly

Theobald Böhm

[*The above is an extract from a personal letter; the original is written in English.*]

PREFACE TO THE SECOND
ENGLISH EDITION

SHORTLY after the publication of the first English edition of "The Flute and Flute-Playing," the translator received a letter dated at Preston, Cuba, April 7, 1909, a portion of which is as follows:

"Dear Sir:—I saw the notice of your work on the Flute, and it interested me for I lived in Munich for three years (beginning May, 1871) and studied flute under Mr. Boehm. I also worked one winter (1872-73) in the shop with Mendler. At that time I translated Mr. Boehm's work on the flute, "Die Flöte und das Flötenspiel," and for doing this he gave me the original manuscript in his own hand writing.   Sincerely,
                           JAMES S. WILKINS, II."

An interesting correspondence developed, and extracts from later letters are as follows:

"I appreciate your efforts in doing reverence to Boehm, to the extent that, at the first safe opportunity I shall send you the original manuscript of "Die Flöte und das Flötenspiel," as a token, in Boehm's name, of my appreciation of the labor you have devoted to his work, and for your excellent translation. I know it would have pleased Mr. Boehm for you to receive it. * * *. I also send you as a part of your collection, a box-wood "Alt-flöte" tube, without keys, made in Mendler's shop; this was given to me by Boehm; it is a sample of a thinned-wood tube with raised finger holes. * * * I am sending a letter Boehm wrote me during a visit to Paris, as well as some leaves from my diary that may interest you—one has Mr. Boehm's autograph with an inscription. * * * I am also sending a biographical article which I wrote in Philadelphia in 1900.

With highest esteem, I am sincerely,
                           JAMES S. WILKINS, II."

Thus the translator came into possession of these most interesting mementos of Boehm, in May,

1909, shortly before the death of Mr. Wilkins. The necessity for a second edition of "The Flute and Flute-Playing," makes it possible to take advantage of this new material.

Boehm's manuscript in German is complete, and has been compared, paragraph by paragraph, with the printed edition; the differences are very few and are of no importance. Boehm's hand writing and his manuscript music are exceedingly neat and legible, as is shown by the reproductions of several pages in this book.

The text here given is a faithful, and usually a very literal, translation of the German. For the second edition the translation has been thoroughly revised so that it reads more smoothly, several hundred minor alterations having been made. Since Boehm's writings possess both a historical and a scientific interest, and his inventions have been the subject of much controversy, it has seemed desirable, in giving his descriptions and explanations, to retain as far as possible, the forms of expression and even the wording of the original. Some traces of the German constructions, no doubt remain. While a freer translation might be preferred by some, it is believed the one given is always intelligible and explicit. There has been a slight rearrangement of subject matter and of paragraphing. The use of emphasis—indicated by *italics* in English—which is very frequent in the original, has been omitted.

Eight errors in the original lithographed Tables of Fingerings, and a few typographical errors in the tables of acoustical numbers have been corrected; no other corrections have been found necessary.

All of the original illustrations, twelve line drawings and several note diagrams, are reproduced with only such alterations as are noted in the descriptive matter; the musical illustrations in Part II have been copied photographically from the German edition. The first English edition contained, in addition, one drawing, several note-diagrams, pictures of six flutes, and three portraits. This edition contains fifty-six illustrations, including the twelve original drawings, pictures of twenty-two flutes, views of Boehm's home, six portraits and facsimiles of manuscripts. There are also several additional drawings and note-diagrams in the text. Two of the three portraits which appeared in the previous edition have been reëngraved from newly found originals. The sources of the portraits are given in the List of Illustrations. All of the pictures of flutes (excepting the two drawings from Boehm's pamphlet of 1847) are photographic reproductions from instruments in the translator's historical collection.

For this edition the Introduction has been rewritten, and four appendices have been added; the latter contain biographical notes, a revised list of Boehm's musical compositions, a price-list of flutes as made by Boehm, and a short list of current books relating to the flute.

In order that the full effect of Boehm's contributions during his life-time, and also that the rela-

tions of these to the flute as it is today, may be
made evident, many annotations and illustrations
have been added to the original text; all such added
matter is enclosed in square brackets, [ ].
Twenty-five or more important annotations and
additions, besides numerous smaller ones, appear
for the first time in this edition. The annotations
have been confined, for the most part, to matters
of fact; while exception has been taken to some
of the opinions expressed by Boehm, this is not
the place for discussion which might lead to controversy. The additions relate largely to details
of dimensions and constructions of the flutes as
made by Boehm & Mendler when these instruments had attained their greatest perfection, in
the years from 1870 to 1880. Nothwithstanding it
is forty years since the death of Boehm, yet there
is published now for the first time, all the essential
dimensions of the flute as Boehm himself made it.
The dimensions are given both for the flute in C
and the flute in G.

While the preparation of this book has involved
much labor, it has been a genuine labor of love;
the volume has become almost a memorial to the
Flute of Boehm. It is hoped that the book will
make still better known Boehm's very careful and
complete investigations, and that it will lead to a
deeper appreciation of the debt of gratitude which
all flutists owe him for the remarkable mechanical
and artistic developments which have resulted
from his efforts.

The writer wishes to express his thanks to Theobald Boehm and his sisters, of Munich, grandchil-

dren of the inventor of the flute; when the writer
first visited them, some years ago, they gave approval of this English edition, and they have very
kindly expressed this sentiment in a letter, a portion of which precedes this preface. These friends
have also given other assistance which is highly
appreciated. He also wishes to thank his many
friends who have very enthusiastically assisted in
the collection of historical material, instruments,
and illustrations, and whose interest in the flute
has been a source of great inspiration and encour-
agement.

DAYTON C. MILLER.

Case School of Applied Science,
Cleveland, Ohio, June, 1922.

CONTENTS

PART II—FLUTE-PLAYING

APPENDIX

LIST OF ILLUSTRATIONS

PORTRAITS

FIGURES

TRANSLATOR'S INTRODUCTION

THEOBALD BOEHM, of Munich—born on April 9, 1794, died on November 25, 1881—a celebrated Royal Bavarian Court-Musician, and inventor of the modern flute, described his inventions in a treatise "Die Flöte und das Flötenspiel," which was published in pamphlet form, in Munich, in 1871. In the introduction to this work Boehm says: "My treatise, 'Ueber den Flötenbau und die neuesten Verbesserungen desselben,' (1847), seems to have had but little influence. There is need, therefore, of this work in which is given as complete a description as is possible of my flutes and instructions for handling them, and which also contains instructions upon the art of playing the flute with a pure tone and a good style."

In a letter to Mr. Broadwood, dated November 15, 1868, Boehm wrote: "I have at length finished it (this treatise) and will see about a publisher. There ought properly to be both a French and an English translation, but I cannot myself undertake them * * * . My treatise will contain chapters as follows: * * * ; and the history of all my work and all my experience during a period of sixty years will be contained in one little book."

"Die Flöte und das Flötenspiel," was read with great interest by the writer, and while upon a holiday some years ago, it was translated; others having expressed a desire to read the work in English, its publication was undertaken, the first English edition appearing in November, 1908.

While much has been written about the Boehm flute, Boehm's own publications seem not to have received the attention they deserve. Boehm submitted his new system flute of 1832 to the Paris Academy of Sciences, where its proper recognition was effectively prevented by the professional jealousy of Coche, who at the same time pretended to be giving friendly assistance. In 1847 Boehm published a small book of 59 pages entitled "Ueber den Flötenbau und die neuesten Verbesserungen desselben." A French translation of this work was published in 1848. Boehm himself prepared an English version which was published in London in 1882, under the title "An Essay on the Construction of Flutes," edited by W. S. Broadwood. Boehm exhibited his new flute with cylindrical bore at the London Exhibitions of 1851 and 1862, and at the Paris Expositions of 1855 and 1867. With the exhibits of 1862 and 1867 he submitted his *Schema* for locating the tone-holes according to a scientific method, the first ever applied to such an instrument. The judges, not appreciating the significance of the *Schema*, refused to recognize it as a meritorious contribution, thus again depriving Boehm of his just rewards. The *Schema* having been discredited by the judges, Boehm's only publication of it was a quite ineffective one in the journal of a local engineering society of Munich, in 1868. In 1871 Boehm published a second work in pamphlet form, "Die Flöte

und das Flötenspiel," the work herewith presented
in translation. After Boehm's death, one of the
judges of the 1867 Exposition, re-examined the
Schema and published, in 1882, his belated conclusion that its method is entirely correct and that
it was actually the basis of Boehm's own constructions.

Several years after Boehm had made known his
flute of 1832 with the new system of fingering, he
was accused, particularly by Coche of Paris, of
having taken important features of his system
from the work of an enthusiastic amateur experi-
menter by the name of Gordon. In answer to this
accusation Boehm wrote in his work of 1847 as
follows: "The surest proof of the authenticity of
my invention, I believe will be given by describ-
ing the motives which led me to its development,
and by explaining the acoustical and mechanical
principles of which I made application; for he
alone is capable of carrying out a rational work,
who is able to give a complete account of the why
and wherefore of every detail from its conception
to its completion." Judged by this criterion, Boehm
deserves the highest credit, for he has given an
account almost beyond criticism, and perhaps the
best ever given for any musical instrument, of
the why and wherefore of the flute.

After Boehm's death, the charge of misappro-
priating Gordon's invention was renewed in a bitter attack by Rockstro in his "Treatise on the
Flute." A very complete account of this controversy and of the historical events mentioned

above, together with a critical analysis of all the evidence, is given in Welch's "History of the Boehm Flute." Welch's investigations completely exonerate Boehm of any improper use of Gordon's work, and fully establish his title to the system which bears his name.

In the pamphlet of 1847 stress was put upon the so-called scientific construction of the flute; in the present treatise the treatment is more complete and practical and the scientific portions appear in truer relations to the subject. To one who reads understandingly it is evident that, while the general treatment of the principles of the flute is a scientific one, the actual dimensions for construction are based upon experiment. Having determined by experiment, the fundamental length of the octave with a flute tube of given dimensions, the locations of all the holes for a flute of any desired pitch are found by the application of simple laws of acoustics. Although no complete set of laws has yet been formulated which enable one to calculate all the dimensions of a flute, this fact in no way lessens the value of Boehm's work. While his greatest desire was to elevate the art of music, he was possessed of the true scientific spirit; his purposes were conceived and carried out according to scientific methods; his finished work was the best practical realization of his ideals and he has described his designs and practical constructions very explicitly. The flute which he revolutionized and developed within a period of fifty years, has not been essentially improved during the subsequent fifty years.

The full consideration of Boehm's contributions must be left for a later work; but to him we certainly owe the present system of fingering—an astonishingly perfect one—the cylinder bore, the silver tube and much of the beautiful mechanism which have completely revolutionized the instrument and have made the Boehm flute one of the most perfect of musical instruments. When one remembers that the flute has been known since prehistoric time, and that its form in the year 1800 is fairly represented by the picture of Boehm's first flute, then a mere glance at the illustration of Boehm's perfected silver flute of 1878, makes it seem almost impossible that such a development could have taken place within the life-time of one man, much less that it could have resulted largely from the investigations and efforts of one man. The musical effects of the flute as perceived by the ear have been improved quite as much as have the mechanical features as seen by the eye. The flute has thus become not only more useful to the professional musician, but it has become an exceedingly attractive and delightful instrument for the amateur. The Boehm flute is, *par excellence,* the instrument for the enthusiastic lover of chamber music.

The flute has always been a favorite instrument with gentlemen performers; it is today, more than ever before, the gentleman's instrument. But the flute of Boehm, made of silver, has an artistic symmetry and beauty, combined with lightness, which renders it as attractive in appearance as it is rich in tone. The sound is produced with the slightest effort; one has only to breathe into the embouchure. The natural position in holding the instrument is characterized by an easy gracefulness; its manipulation in general requires delicacy of manner. Boehm's improvements have greatly enhanced these qualities, and now the flute is preeminently suited for use as a lady's instrument.

One of Boehm's real contributions which the musical world has been slow to appreciate, is the flute in G, the Bass Flute. Boehm made this instrument entirely practicable for musical purposes, and it has tonal qualities that should have given it prominence long ago. It is hoped that not only flutists, but composers, directors, and auditors, will very soon realize the beauties of this instrument, and that its use will be greatly stimulated.

While this work is devoted to the flute, yet flutists will the better realize the value of Boehm's contributions, by keeping in mind the fact that they were of wide application. His researches in connection with the flute and its theory played an important part in the development of other instruments, such as the clarinet, oboe, and bassoon. No history of these instruments can be complete without including references to Boehm's work. He contributed to a very important phase of the development of the modern piano, the method of "overstringing." Boehm spent several years in investigations quite foreign to the world of music, in the development of improved methods for the purification of iron and for the manufacture of steel directly from iron; his contributions were certainly of fundamental importance. He also invented a new device for transmitting rotatory motion, which, if not important, is interesting and was deemed worthy of a silver medal. Several of these diverse interests are referred to in the Appendix.

Boehm was an extraordinary artist, and he was possessed of the true scientific spirit of research; he was a man of great versatility and of profound mental ability: he is more than worthy of all the honor that he has received.

PART I

—

THE FLUTE

Die Flöte und das Flötenspiel,

in akustischer, technischer und artistischer Beziehung.

von

Theobald Boehm.

Die Flöte.

Nach dem System von Theobald Boehm in München.

Einleitung.

Es sind nun über 60 Jahre verflossen, seit ich auf meiner ersten selbst verfertigten Flöte zu spielen begann. Ich war damals ein tüchtiger Goldarbeiter und auch in mechanischen Arbeiten wohl geübt. Es gelang mir daher bald einige wesentliche Verbesserungen an den Klappen, Federn und Polstern meiner Flöten zu machen; allein alle meine Bemühungen, Gleichheit der Töne und Reinheit der Stimmung herzustellen waren erfolglos, so lange die Spannweite der Finger zur Einbohrung der Tonlöcher maßgebend blieb.

Diese mußten in entsprechender Größe auf ihre akustisch richtigeren Standpunkte gebracht, und sodann ein ganz neues Griff-system geschaffen werden.

Eine solche Reform der Flöte konnte ich jedoch nicht vornehmen, ohne meine, durch zwanzigjährige Übung erlangte Fertigkeit im Spiele zum Opfer zu bringen.

Fig. 1.

This plate is a photographic reproduction, slightly reduced in size, of the title page and part of page 1 of the original manuscript in Boehm's handwriting, of the work here presented. How this came into the translator's possession is told in the preface.

THE FLUTE
AND FLUTE-PLAYING

PART I—THE FLUTE

UPON THE SYSTEM OF

THEOBALD BOEHM

OF MUNICH

I. INTRODUCTION

IT is now more than sixty years since I began
to play upon the first flute of my own construction. I was at that time a proficient goldsmith
and was also skilled in the mechanic arts. I soon
endeavored to make essential improvements in the
keys, springs, and pads of my flute; but, notwithstanding all my efforts, equality of tone and perfection of tuning were impossible, because the
proper spacing of the tone-holes required too great
a spreading of the fingers. In order that the tone-
holes might be made of proper size and be placed
at the acoustically correct points, it was necessary
to devise an entirely new system of fingering. The
application of this system required a remodeling
of the flute which I was unable to accomplish
without sacrificing my facility in playing which
had been acquired by twenty years of practice.

["As a child Boehm was charmed by music, and
he learned by himself to play the flageolet; when

Fig. 2.
Boehm's first flute, played by him when
he was about fifteen years old

this no longer satisfied him, he took up the flute."
Fig. 2 is a picture of what was probably Boehm's
first flute, here referred to. This instrument has
recently been obtained from Mr. Franz Rath of
San Diego, California, and is now in the translator's historical collection of flutes. Mr. Rath
supplies the following information. Boehm owned
this flute in his boyhood; as his proficiency developed he needed a flute with more keys, and
about 1810, when he was sixteen years old, he
sold this one to his chum, Ferinand Marker. Herr
Marker removed to Vienna about 1820, and later
taught his grandson, Franz Rath, to play the flute
and gave him the old flute of Boehm's about 1874.
Mr. Rath came to America in 1887 bringing the
flute with him, and it has remained in his possession till the present time, 1920. The flute is of
boxwood, stained and cracked, as might be expected after having served several young flute
players. The maker's name, PROSER, is stamped on
each joint. "At the age of sixteen years (in 1810)
he made for himself an instrument patterned after
one with four keys, (from the workshop of the
celebrated Karl August Grenser of Dresden),
which had been loaned him by a friend. Then
he began to blow the flute with gleeful enthusiasm
in all his spare time, not especially to the delight
of his friends and neighbors. Among them was
Johann Nepomuk Capeller, at that time flutist in
the Court Orchestra, who, one day, happened to
meet the budding virtuoso on the stairway and
he laughingly said: 'You, young flute-player, I cannot endure your noisy blowing any longer; come

to me and I will show you how it ought to be done.'
Naturally it was not necessary to say this twice to
young Boehm. He became Capeller's most zealous
pupil and, notwithstanding he had but little time
to devote to the flute, his passionate fondness for
the instrument caused such rapid progress that,
after scarcely two years of practice, he created
astonishment by public performances." — The
quoted sentences have been translated from the
privately-printed booklet, *Zur Erinnerung an
Theobald Boehm,* presented by Boehm's grandchildren. Much the same account is given in
Schafhäutl's "Life of Boehm," which is a part
of Welch's "History of the Boehm Flute."]

["With my progress in flute-playing there developed, naturally, a desire for better instruments.
In 1812 I was already the first flutist in the Royal
Isarthor Theater in Munich. In the years between
this and 1817, by using the facilities of my goldsmith's shop which had the usual equipment and
which was further supplied with the necessary
machinery, I made many flutes, for myself and
others, according to the best models of the time
and also with many original improvements * *
such as new types of springs, linings and corks
for the joints, a moveable gold embouchure, and
others. After I obtained my appointment to the
Royal Court Chapel in 1818 the business of goldsmith was given up and I devoted myself entirely
to music. For some years, because of the lack of
my own shop, I had flutes made according to my
designs by other makers; however, the instruments
thus obtained were not satisfactory, and, finally,

in order to carry out my own ideas without hindrance, I decided to establish my own flute factory. In October, 1828, I was again at work in my well-equipped shop, and began to construct various machines and appliances for making with more facility and accuracy a better key mechanism than had previously been in use. Among these devices was one for screwing the metal posts into the wood accurately in the line of radius of the bore; another was for boring the holes in the spherical heads of the pillars. These and numerous other devices secured the easy and certain operation of all parts of the mechanism. By the end of the year the first flute was finished, having a new key mechanism which was both solid and elegant in construction, and the flute met with general approbation as to quality of tone and intonation, and was widely adopted. In the year 1831 I played in Paris and London upon such a flute of the ordinary system which had been made in my workshop in Munich."—From Boehm's pamphlet of 1847, *Ueber den Flötenbau und die neuesten Verbesserungen desselben*. Fig. 3 is the drawing of this flute which accompanies the above description, and to which Boehm has attached the date 1829. In February, 1922, the translator received from Mr. Arthur Gemeinhardt of Markneukirchen, a rare specimen of this identical type, made in Boehm's shop, which is shown in Fig. 5. This flute is of cocus-wood, with silver keys and flat gold springs, with workmanship and finish which are perfect; it is certainly superior to any other contemporary flute which has been examined, and comparable with the later instruments of Boehm & Mendler. The tone is very beautiful, sweet and mellow, and, of course, not powerful; the tuning is astonishingly good considering that it is a flute of the old system. The flute bears the inscription BOEHM & GREVE A MUNICH. Grevé was Boehm's chief workman and partner, and is known to have been with him at least from 1830 to 1843.]

Notwithstanding all my success as an artist, the defects of my instrument remained perceptible, and finally I decided, in 1832, to construct my ring-keyed flute, upon which I played in London and Paris in the following year, where its advantages were at once recognized by the greatest artists and by *l'Académie des sciences.*

[In a letter to Mr. Broadwood, dated August, 1871, Boehm writes: "I did as well as any continental flutist could have done, in London, in 1831, but I could not match Nicholson in power of tone, wherefore I set to work to remodel my flute. Had I not heard him, probably the Boehm flute would never have been made."]

As compared with the old flute, this one was unquestionably much nearer perfection. The tone-holes were placed in their acoustically correct position and, through my new system of fingering, one could play all possible tone combinations clearly and surely. As regards the sounding and the quality of the lower and the higher tones, there was yet much to be desired, but further improvements could be secured only by a complete change in the bore of the flute tube.

FIG. 3.   Boehm's Flute
Old System. 1829.

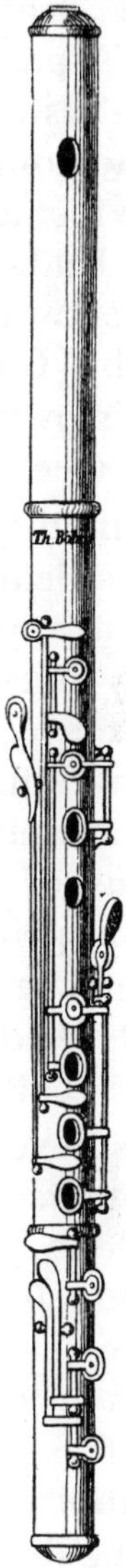

FIG. 4.   Boehm's Flute
New System. 1832.

[The drawing, Fig. 4, is reproduced from Boehm's pamphlet of 1847, and shows the first Boehm-System Flute, originated in 1832, with ring-keys and conical bore. Boehm made arrangements to have his new-system flute manufactured in London by Rudall and Rose and in Paris by Godfroy. Fig. 6 shows an excellent specimen of this type made by Godfroy about 1840. It differs from Boehm's own model only in that it has the Dorus G♯ key (see page 64) instead of the open G♯ key.]

The method of boring, with a cylindrical head and a conical contraction in the lower part, which was first applied by Christopher Denner of Nuremberg (born in 1655, died in 1707), and later was improved by Quantz [1697-1773], Tromlitz [1726-1805], and others, was nevertheless far from being in accordance with acoustical principles, as the positions of the finger-holes had been borrowed from the primitive *Schwegel* or *Querpfeife*. This conical bore was in use for more than a century and a half, during which time no one was able to devise a better form.

I was never able to understand why, of all wind instruments with tone-holes and conical bore, the flute alone should be blown at its wider end; it seems much more natural that, with a rising pitch and shorter length of air column, the diameter should become smaller. I experimented with tubes of various bores but I soon found that, with only empirical experiments, a satisfactory result would be difficult of attainment.

[The flute of 1832 with conical bore and ring

FIG. 5.
Old-System Flute
by Boehm & Grevé
Model of 1829

FIG. 6.
Boehm-System Flute
by Godfroy
Model of 1840

FIG. 7.
Cylinder Flute No. 19
by Th. Boehm
Model of 1850

keys, therefore, remained unchanged for fifteen years. Boehm says in his treatise of 1847: "With regard to all the other alterations or improvements which have since been made in the flute (between the years 1832 and 1846), whose value or worthlessness I leave for others to decide, I had no part in them. From the year 1833 to the year 1846 I was unable to devote my time to the manufacture of instruments, being otherwise engaged [in iron and steel work] and for this reason my flute factory was·given up eight years ago, in 1839."]

I finally called science to my aid and gave two years [1846-1847] to the study of the principles of acoustics under the excellent guidance of Herr Professor Dr. Carl von Schafhäutl [of the University of Munich. An account of Schafhäutl's life and work by Herr Ludwig Boehm appeared in the *Bayer Industrie und Gewerbeblatt,* No. 17, 1890. A translation of this memoir is given in Welch's "History of the Boehm Flute," pages 348-372]. After making many experiments, as precise as possible, I finished a flute in the later part of 1847, founded upon scientific principles, for which I received the highest prize at the World's Expositions, in London in 1851, and in Paris in 1855.

[Fig. 7 is a picture of the metal flute with cylindrical bore and covered keys invented in 1847. This instrument, made by Boehm himself, is No. 19 of the series beginning in 1847. It belonged to Edward Martin Heindl, one of Boehm's most famous pupils, who lived with Boehm for four years from 1847 to 1851. Heindl came to America in

1864, bringing this flute, which is probably the first cylinder-bore, metal Boehm flute used in this country. Heindl played this instrument for many years while he was a member of the Mendelssohn Quintette Club of Boston, and after he became first flutist of the Boston Symphony Orchestra, upon its organization in 1881. See pages 28, 95 and 99.]

Since this time my flutes have come to be played in all the countries of the world, yet my treatise, *Ueber den Flötenbau und die neuesten Verbesserungen desselben,* published before that time [in 1847] by B. Schott's Söhne of Mainz, which contains complete explanations of my system with the dimensions and numerical proportions, seems to have had but little influence. Because of the many questions which are continually being asked of me concerning the advantages and management of my flute, it is evident that the acoustical proportions and key mechanism are not sufficiently well understood to enable one to help himself in case of accidental troubles and derangements.

There is need, therefore, of this work, which will be welcomed by all flute players, in which is given as complete a description as is possible of my flutes, and instructions for handling them, and which also contains instructions upon the art of playing the flute with a pure tone and a good style.

II. THE ACOUSTICAL PROPORTIONS OF THE FLUTE

[The original manuscript of this work contains a page which has been crossed out by a pencil mark, and which does not appear in the first printed edition. While this portion, consisting of the first three following paragraphs, is not important, nevertheless it forms an appropriate introduction to this chapter.]

ALL of my flutes consist of three pieces, the head-joint, the middle-joint, and the foot. When these pieces are joined together they form the tube of the flute, which is closed above the mouth-hole by a cork plug. The main part of the tube is cylindrical, with an inside diameter of 19 millimeters. The bore of the head-joint is gradually reduced in diameter by two millimeters, from the joint upwards to the cork. The free speech of the tone and the correct tuning of the higher octaves depend upon the particular form of this curvilinear reduction in the diameter.

The air column enclosed by the tube of the flute is set into vibration by blowing across the mouth-hole, causing the fundamental tone to sound. The pitch of this tone depends upon the total length of the vibrating column of air measured from the cork to the lower end of the tube. The higher tones of the first octave are obtained by shortening the length of the vibrating column of air, for which purpose lateral tone-holes are bored in the tube. The holes should be as large as is possible, since the effective shortening of the tube is proportional to the ratio of the size of the hole to the diameter of the bore.

The correct intonation of a tone depends, consequently, not only upon the distance of the hole from the upper end of the air column, but also upon its size, and therefore the exact place where the hole is located must be determined by accurate computation. All the formulae for these calculations, as well as other theoretical explanations have previously been given in my treatise *Ueber den Flötenbau,* already mentioned.

[The metric system is used throughout in giving the dimensions of the flute. For conversion, the following equivalents may be used: 1 inch=25.40 millimeters; 1 millimeter=0.03937 inch; 1 ounce avoirdupois=28.35 grams; 1 ounce Troy=31.10 grams].

All wind instruments with tone- or finger-holes, whose construction requires very accurate proportions, can be improved only through the investigation of the principles of both the good and the bad of existing instruments, and through a rational application of the results; the greatest possible perfection will be obtained only when theory and practice go hand in hand. When the calculation of the required data is undertaken, the questions first to be investigated are the dimensions and numerical proportions of the air columns and tone-holes of each separate instrument.

For this purpose I had prepared, in 1846, a great number of conical and cylindrical tubes of various dimensions, and of many metals and several kinds of wood, so that the relative fitness of each as to pitch, ease of sounding and quality of tone, could be fundamentally investigated.

The most desirable proportions of the air column, that is, the dimensions of bore best suited for bringing out the fundamental tones at various pitches, were soon found. These experiments show:

1. That the strength, as well as the full, clear quality of the fundamental tone, is proportional to the volume of the air set in vibration.

2. That a more or less important contraction in the bore of the upper part of the flute tube, and a shortening or lengthening of this contraction, have an important influence upon the production of the tones and upon the tuning of the octaves.

3. That this contraction must be made in a certain geometrical proportion, which is closely approached by the curve of the parabola.

4. That the formation of the nodes and segments of the sound waves takes place most easily and perfectly in a cylindrical flute tube, the length of which is thirty times its diameter, and in which the contraction begins in the upper fourth part of the length of the tube, continuing to the cork where the diameter is reduced one tenth part.

[Perhaps flutists are more puzzled by the "parabolic head-joint" than by any other feature of the modern flute. The contraction in the bore is undoubtedly determined by experiment, and not by any mathematical calculation based upon the properties of the parabola. The translator has measured and plotted the curves of perhaps a hundred flutes, among which are specimens of nearly every celebrated make. Most of these curves do not in any way resemble a parabola; such resemblance as is possessed by the few may be described by saying that the curve which at first departs but little from the straight line, bends more and more rapidly as it progresses. But sometimes the portion with the greatest curvature is next to the cork and sometimes next to the tuning slide!]

[The "parabolic" contraction in the head-joint of an excellent specimen of Boehm & Mendler flute is shown in Fig. 8. At the right is the section of the tube, drawn in full size. The length of the tapered portion is 134 millimeters. Starting at the cork, where the diameter of the bore is 17.1 millimeters, the horizontal dotted lines indicate the sections increasing in diameter, successively, by 0.1 millimeter, up to 19.0 millimeters, near the tuning slide. The figures on the dotted lines are the diameters of the tube at the various sections. At the left is an exaggerated diagram of the actual contraction in this specimen of flute; the horizontal scale for this part of the figure is 50 times the vertical scale. If the bore of the tube were

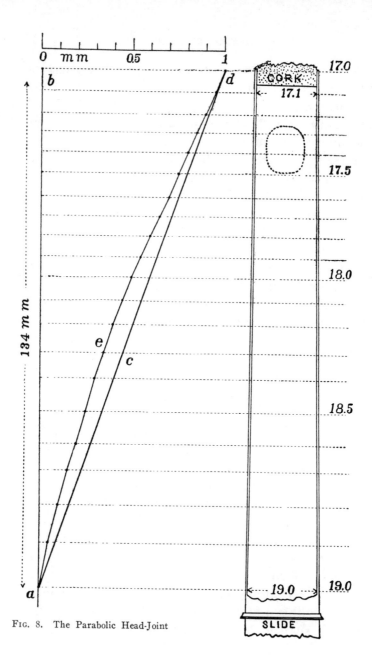

FIG. 8. The Parabolic Head-Joint

cylindrical, one side of it would be represented by the line *ab;* if it contracted by a straight taper, the line *acd* would represent the inner surface of the tube; the "parabolic" curve actually existing is shown by the curved line *aed.*]

Since the dimensions most suitable for the formation of the fundamental tones correspond closely to those of theory, a flute of these dimensions, the length of the air column being 606 millimeters and the diameter 20 millimeters, [because of the larger diameter, the length of tube required is somewhat less than that given on page 35 for a tube 19 millimeters in diameter] would certainly be perfect as regards a pure, full tone and ease of sounding through a compass of about two octaves. But in order to extend the compass to three full octaves as now required [in flute music] I decided for the sake of freedom in the upper tones, to reduce the diameter to 19 millimeters, notwithstanding that this injured to some extent the beauty of the tones of the first two octaves.

[In a letter written in 1867 Boehm says: "I have made several flutes with a bore 20 millimeters in diameter, therefore one millimeter wider than usual; the first and second octaves were better, but of course the third octave was not so good. I could, indeed still play up to C_6, but from $F_5\sharp$ upwards the notes were sounded with difficulty, and if my lip did not happen to be in good order, I could not sound the higher notes *piano* at all. The flute, whether in the orchestra or in solo playing, is treated as the next highest instrument after the piccolo; modern composers do not hesitate to write for it up to C_6; therefore the bore of 19 millimeters diameter is certainly the best for general purposes."]

[The silver flute with a wood head-joint which is shown in Fig. 32 has a bore of 20 millimeters; it is the only flute in C of this bore which the translator has seen. Its tone quality has been directly compared with that of other Boehm & Mendler flutes having a bore of 19 millimeters. The result of the comparison was to corroborate the opinions of Boehm as expressed above.]

[Before the year 1865 Boehm had developed the "Alt-Flöte," commonly called the "Bass Flute," which is described in Chapter XII; the tube of this instrument has an inside diameter of 26 millimeters. Messrs. Rudall, Carte and Company have long made such bass flutes and also the "Alto Flute" in B♭, having a bore of 20.5 millimeters. These instruments are altogether practicable and have the beautiful tone quality in the lower octaves, referred to above.]

A second obstacle which compelled me to depart from the theory was the impossibility of making a movable cork or stopper in the upper end of the flute, so that its distance from the center of the embouchure might be decreased or increased in proportion to the pitch of each tone; a medium position for it must therefore be chosen which will best serve for both the highest and the lowest tones; this position was found to be 17 millimeters from the center of the embouchure.

Next, the size and form of the mouth-hole (embouchure) must be determined. The tone-producing current of air must be blown against the sharp edge of the mouth-hole, at an angle which varies with the pitch of the tone. When the air stream strikes the edge of the hole it is broken, or rather divided, so that one part of it goes over or beyond the hole, while the greater part, especially with a good embouchure, produces tone and acts upon the column of air enclosed by the tube, setting it into vibration.

By this means the molecular vibrations [see page 53] of the tube are excited, producing a tone as long as the air stream is maintained; it follows therefore that the tone will be stronger the greater the number of the air particles acting upon the tone-producing air column in a given time. The opening between the lips through which the stream of air passes is in the form of a slit, and a mouth-hole in shape like an elongated rectangle with rounded corners, presenting a long edge to the wide air stream, will allow more air to be effective than would a round or oval hole of equal size.

[Figs. 9 and 10 are photographs of the embouchures of two excellent flutes, shown somewhat larger than full size, representing the oval and rounded-square shapes. The latter is a perfect specimen of the Boehm & Mendler type. The selection of shape and size of embouchure seems to be largely one of individual choice or habit; an embouchure which one performer finds to be excellent another cannot use.]

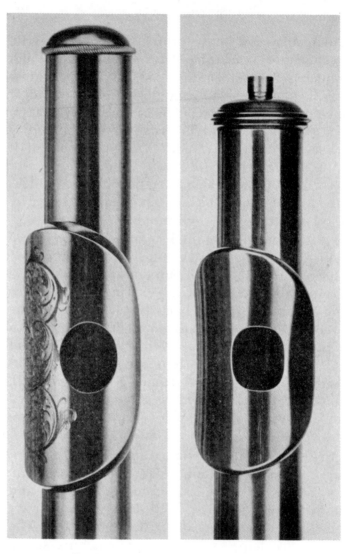

FIG. 9.
Elliptical Embouchure
Rudall, Carte & Co.

FIG. 10.
Rectangular Embouchure
Boehm & Mendler

For the same reason a larger mouth-hole will produce a louder tone than a smaller one, but this requires a greater strength in the muscles of the lip, because there is formed a hollow space under the lip which is unsupported. More than this, it is often difficult to keep the air current directed at the proper angle, upon which the intonation and the tone quality for the most part depend.

By a greater depression of the air stream towards the middle of the hole, the tone becomes deeper and more pungent, while a greater elevation makes the tone higher and more hollow. Consequently the angle between the sides of the mouth-hole and the longitudinal section through the axis of the air column, as well as the height of these sides, has an important influence upon the easy production of the tone. In my opinion an angle of 7 degrees is best adapted to the entire compass of tones, the walls being 4.2 millimeters

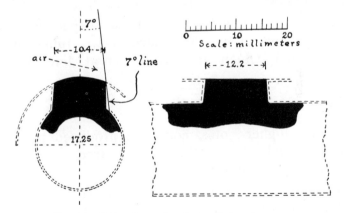

Fig. 11.   Embouchure of a Boehm & Mendler flute.
Transverse and longitudinal sections.

thick; and a mouth-hole 10 millimeters wide and 12 millimeters long, is best suited to most flute players.

[The measurements of many Boehm & Mendler flutes show sizes slightly larger than that mentioned, the average being 10.4 millimeters by 12.2 millimeters (0.409 inch by 0.480 inch).]

[The shape of a blow-hole may be clearly seen from a wax impression; Fig. 11 shows transverse and longitudinal sections of a gold embouchure on a Boehm & Mendler flute. The cut is made photographically from the actual wax casts, and is slightly larger than full size. This blow-hole has sides which are straight and nearly parallel. The 7° of undercutting mentioned by Boehm, indicated by the solid line in the figure, is not present. Some of the earlier flutes by Boehm show a slight undercutting, but the later ones, both of wood and silver, have the sides nearly parallel, as shown in this instance.]

Upon the completion of these experiments I constructed many thin, hard-drawn tubes of brass upon which the fundamental tone C_3,

and also higher notes, could be produced by a breath and be brought to any desired strength without their rising in pitch.

The fact that the hissing noise heard in other flutes was not perceptible convinced me that the correct dimensions of the tube, and its smooth inner surface permitted the formation of the sound waves without noticeable friction. From this as well as from the fine quality of tone of the harmonics or acoustical over-tones, can be inferred the perfect fitness of my tube for the flute; and with this I began the determination of the amount of shortening or cutting of the air column, required for producing the intervals of the first octave.

The simplest and shortest method is, naturally, successively to cut off from the lower end of the flute tube so much as will make the length of the air column correspond to each tone of the chromatic scale. In order that these proportions might be accurately verified, I made a tube in which all the twelve tone sections could be taken off and again put together, and which was provided with a sliding joint in the upper part of the tube to correct for any defects in tuning.

Since a flute cannot be made to consist of many separate pieces, all the tone lengths must be combined in one tube and these lengths must be determined by laterally bored holes; the air column may be considered as disconnected or cut off by these holes in a degree determined by the ratio between the diameters of the holes and of the tube.

The effective air column, however, is not as much shortened by a tone-hole as it would be by cutting the tube at the same point. Even if the size of the hole is equal to the diameter of the tube, yet the air waves will not pass out of the hole at a right angle as freely as along the axis.

ABIGAIL E. WEEKS MEMORIAL LIBRARY
UNION COLLEGE
BARBOURVILLE, KENTUCKY

The waves meet with a resistance from the air contained in the lower part of the tube, which is so considerable that all the tones are much too flat when they come from holes placed at the points determined by actually cutting the tube. And, moreover, the height of the sides of the holes adds to the flattening effect. The tone-holes must, therefore, be placed nearer the mouth-hole the smaller their diameter and the higher their sides.

Although one octave can be correctly tuned in this manner using small holes, yet for the following reasons it is greatly to be desired that the tone-holes should be as large as possible.

1. Free and therefore powerful tones can be obtained only from large holes which are placed as nearly as possible in their acoustically correct positions.

2. If the holes are small and are considerably removed from their proper places, the formation of the nodes of vibration is disturbed and rendered uncertain; the tone is produced with difficulty, and often breaks into other tones corresponding to the other aliquot parts of the air column [harmonics].

3. The smaller the holes, the more distorted become the tone waves, rendering the tone dull and of poor quality.

4. The pure intonation of the third octave depends particularly upon the correct position of the holes.

From accurate investigations it is shown that the disadvantages just mentioned, become imperceptible only when the size of the holes is, at the least, three-fourths of the diameter of the tube [14¼ millimeters]. But in the manufacture of wooden flutes, the making of holes of such a size causes considerable difficulty. At first it appeared very desirable to make the holes of gradually increasing size from the upper to the lower ones; later this proved to be very disadvantageous and again I concluded that a medium course is the best. Therefore I finally chose a constant diameter for all the twelve tone-holes from $C_3^\sharp$ to C_4, which for silver flutes is 13.5 millimeters, and for wooden flutes 13 millimeters.

[Actual measurements of many Boehm & Mendler flutes usually show tone-holes for both the body and foot-joints of wooden flutes which are uniformly 12.8 millimeters in diameter. A few flutes only have holes full 13 millimeters in diameter. The largest size of hole found on the body-joint of a silver flute is 13.4 millimeters, while the usual size is 13.2 millimeters for both body and foot-joint. The Macauley flute, Fig. 31, No. 12, and also Fig. 34, has holes on the body (nine holes) 13.2 millimeters in diameter, while the four holes on the B♮ foot-joint are 14.5 millimeters in diameter. This enlargement of the holes on the foot-joint is seldom found on Boehm's flutes, but it is common in flutes of modern manufacture. The Shippen flute, Fig. 31, No. 13, and also Fig. 32, with a bore 20 millimeters, has the five upper holes on the body (G♯, A, A♯, B, and C thumb-key) of a diameter of 14.0 millimeters while the four lower holes on the body and the four holes on the B♮ foot-joint have a uniform diameter of 15 millimeters.]

[The Heindl flute, illustrated in Fig. 7 and in the group picture, Fig. 31, was made about 1850, and has graduated tone-holes. The thumb-key hole for C_4 is 11.4 millimeters in diameter, and the low C♯ hole is 13.6 millimeters in diameter; the sizes of the holes increase uniformly, each being 0.2 millimeter larger in diameter than the preceding hole. A letter written by Boehm, in 1862, to Louis Lot, the celebrated flute-maker of Paris, says regarding graduated tone-holes: "The flute-playing world knows that for six years I made all my silver flutes with graduated holes. During my stay in London in 1851, I, myself, used a flute with graduated holes. The smallest, the thumb-key hole for C_4 was 12 millimeters in diameter, and the largest, that for C_3♯, 15 millimeters, a constant gradation of a quarter of a millimeter. The graduated holes are in my opinion the best, but the difference is scarcely appreciable. I have discontinued making them on account of the greater difficulty in the manufacture." The last sentence seems to state three facts regarding graduated holes; they are the best; their superiority is slight; the cost of manufacture is greater. Today nearly all makers use at least two sizes of holes, and some use three or more sizes, for the regular tone-holes.]

With these dimensions, in order to produce the correct pitch, the center of the C_3♯ hole must be moved 5 millimeters above the point at which the tube would have to be cut off in order to produce the same tone. The amount of removal increases with each hole in the ascending scale, so that the C_4 hole [thumb-key hole] must be placed 12 millimeters above the point of section of the air column. In this manner the correct positions of the holes are obtained, and the tuning of all the notes of the first octave is rendered, to the ear, as perfect as possible.

The notes of the second octave are produced, as it were, by overblowing the tones of the first, by narrowing the opening in the lips, and by changing the angle and increasing the speed of the stream of air; this results in the formation of shorter tone-waves.

In order to secure a greater compass of tones [in the higher octaves], it is necessary to use a narrower tube than is best suited to the lower tones, or, in other words, a tube which has a diameter too small in proportion to its length. From this it results that the tones D_4 and D_4#

[being sounded as harmonics of a long, slender tube] are of different quality from the next following tones, and it is first with the tone E_4 that a suitable relation between the length and width of the tube is again restored.

The flute properly should have three additional large holes for the tones C_4#, D_4, D_4#.

Following the theory, the octave holes for D_4 and $D_4\sharp$ would also serve as vent holes for the twelfths, $G_5\sharp$ and A_5, giving all of these tones a better quality, a purer intonation, and a freer sounding. But there is only one finger available, and this must be used for $C_4\sharp$; and as I was unwilling to make my key system still more complicated, the $C_4\sharp$ hole must be so placed that it may serve at the same time as a so-called vent hole for the tones, D_4, $D_4\sharp$, D_5, $G_5\sharp$, and A_5.

[Thus the theoretical position of the $C_4\sharp$ hole was abandoned] and it was necessary to determine by experiment a size and position for the $C_4\sharp$ hole which would satisfy all of these demands. It was found that the $C_4\sharp$ hole, as well as the two small holes for the D_4 and $D_4\sharp$ trill-keys, must therefore be placed considerably above their true positions, and must be made correspondingly smaller. [The sizes and positions of these holes are given on page 35.]

For the exact determination of these positions and the other tuning proportions, I had a flute made with movable holes, and was thus enabled to adjust all the tones higher or lower at pleasure. In this way I could easily determine the best positions of the upper three small holes, but it was not possible to determine the tuning of the other tones as perfectly as I desired; for, in endeavoring to produce an entire true scale in one key, the tones were always thrown out of the proportions of the equal temperament, without which the best possible tuning of wind instruments with tone-holes cannot be obtained.

Therefore, in order to determine with perfect accuracy the points at which the tone-holes shall be bored, one must avail himself of the help of theory. To form a basis for all the calculations of dimensions, and for the easy understanding of this, it seems not out of place to give as simply as possible an explanation of the fundamental acoustical laws.

As is known, the acuteness or graveness of a tone depends upon the length and volume of the sounding body, being proportional to the velocity of vibration which can be impressed upon the body. For the entire compass of musical tones, these fixed relative proportions have long been known with mathematical precision; the following Table I gives these relations for all the tones of the equally tempered scale in the form of vibration numbers and string lengths. [The ratio of the number of vibrations of any tone in the equally tempered scale to the number of vibrations of the preceding tone is the twelfth root of 2; the numerical value of this ratio is 1.059463. As the numbers in this table are useful for various acoustical computations, they have been recomputed by the translator, and several typographical errors in Boehm's figures have been corrected.]

TABLE I

Tones	Relative Vibration Numbers	Relative String Lengths
C_{x+1}	2.000000	0.500000
B	1.887749	0.529732
B♭ or A♯	1.781797	0.561231
A	1.681793	0.594604
A♭ or G♯	1.587401	0.629960
G	1.498307	0.667420
G♭ or F♯	1.414214	0.707107
F	1.334840	0.749154
E	1.259921	0.793701
E♭ or D♯	1.189207	0.840896
D	1.122462	0.890899
D♭ or C♯	1.059463	0.943874
C_x	1.000000	1.000000

Here is shown the geometrical progression in which the vibration frequency of C_x, which is designated the fundamental, is constantly increased throughout the scale, so that the number of vibrations of the octave, C_{x+1} has become double that of C_x; at the same time, shortening in equal progression, the string length is reduced from 1.0 to 0.5.

With these relative numbers it is a simple matter to calculate the absolute vibration-numbers corresponding to any desired pitch, since any given vibration number bears to each of the other intervals exactly the same proportion, as the relative number corresponding to this tone bears to the relative numbers of these other intervals.

For example, to calculate the number of vibrations of the tone C_3, knowing the absolute number of vibrations of the Normal A_3 to be 435 vibrations per second we have the following proportion:

relative A_3 : relative C_3=absolute A_3 : absolute C_3

$$1.681793 : 1.000000 = 435 : x$$

$$\frac{435 \times 1.000000}{1.681793} = 258.65$$

If now this absolute number 258.65 be multiplied by each of the relative vibration numbers of the above table, one obtains the absolute vibration numbers of all the tones in one octave of the normal scale from C_3 to C_4 [see Table II, page 35]. In this way one avoids the division by numbers of many places, which is necessary in the direct method of calculation.

In a similar way one calculates measurements of length, as soon as the theoretical length of the air column in any given system, corresponding to the string length 1.000000, is determined.

While the vibration numbers and theoretical proportions of lengths for all instruments remain always the same, yet the actual lengths of the air columns are very different, because each wind instrument has its own peculiar length in consequence of its method of tone formation. For example, an oboe and likewise a clarinet (on account of the flattening effect upon the tone of the tube and mouth-piece) are much shorter than a flute of the same pitch; and even in the flute the actual length of the air column is less than the theoretical length corresponding to the given tone. The same is true to a less extent of a simple tube or a mouth-piece alone. Hence it happens that a wind instrument cut in two in its middle does not given the octave of its fundamental, but a considerably flatter tone.

In the case of the flute the flattening influence of the cork, the mouth-hole, the tone-holes, and the dimensions of bore is such that, altogether, it amounts to an air column of 51.5 millimeters in length, which in the calculation must be considered theoretically as existing, in order that the length of the air column shall exactly correspond to the length of the string of the monochord determined from the numbers and proportions of the table.

It will be found that the actual length of the air column (and therefore also of the flute tube) from the center of a C_3 hole, bored in the side of a long flute tube [or, from the center of the $C\natural$ hole in a $B\natural$ or a $B\flat$ foot-joint] to the face of the cork is 618.5 millimeters, and that the length of the first octave from the center of the hole for C_3 to the center of the hole for C_4 is 335 millimeters; thus the upper portion is 51.5 millimeters shorter than the lower, and in calculating, this quantity (51.5 millimeters) must be taken into consideration. [This quantity may be called the "closed-end correction" for this particular size of tube (see page 42).]

By doubling the length of the octave one obtains as the theoretical air column the length of 670 millimeters, which serves as the unit of calculation, and from which, corresponding to the normal pitch [A=435], are obtained the following absolute vibration-numbers and the relative and the actual length-measures. [All the dimensions in this table and throughout this text, which refer to the positions of tone-holes are measured from the *centers* of the holes. The numbers in this table have been recomputed by the translator. The numbers of vibrations for the tones for the next lower octave are obtained by dividing the numbers in the first column by two, and for the higher octave by multiplying by two; the theoretical lengths of the air column for the next lower octave are obtained from the second column by multiplying by two, and for the higher octave by dividing by two. The actual lengths of air column for other octaves cannot be obtained by this simple process, but must be determined by experiment.]

TABLE II

Tones	Absolute Vibration Numbers	Theoretical Lengths of Air Column	Actual Lengths of Air Column
C_4	517.31	335.00mm	283.50mm
B_3	488.27	354.92	303.42
$B_3\flat$ $A_3\sharp$	460.87	376.02	324.52
A_3	435.00	398.38	346.88
$A_3\flat$ $G_3\sharp$	410.59	422.07	370.57
G_3	387.54	447.17	395.67
$G_3\flat$ $F_3\sharp$	365.79	473.76	422.26
F_3	345.26	501.93	450.43
E_3	325.88	531.78	480.28
$E_3\flat$ $D_3\sharp$	307.59	563.40	511.90
D_3	290.33	596.90	545.40
$D_3\flat$ $C_3\sharp$	274.03	632.40	580.90
C_3	258.65	670.00	618.50

Evidently for the practical application, 51.5 millimeters must be subtracted from each of the theoretical lengths to obtain the actual lengths, given in the third column, which determine the distances between the face of the cork and the center points for boring the tone-holes. [See the diagram on page 41.]

[The center of the blow-hole is 17.00 millimeters from the face of the cork. The center of the C_4 hole (the thumb-key hole) is 283.50 millimeters from the cork. The distance of 618.50 millimeters for the C_3 hole is for a lateral tone-hole in a tube which extends downwards to B♮ or lower. If the flute is in C, then this tone is given by the open end. As mentioned on page 29, the distance between the center of the C_3♯ hole and the end of the tube is found by experiment to be 5 millimeters greater than the distance to the center of a hole for C_3 located by the simple theory, hence it follows that the open end for C_3 is $618.50+5.00=623.50$ millimeters from the face of the cork.]

[The center of a tone-hole for C_3 is 618.50 millimeters from the cork. Extending the *Schema,* the distance of the center of a lateral tone-hole for B♮ (foot-joint) is 658.32 millimeters. If this tone is given by the open end, the correction is $+5.30$ millimeters, and the distance of the open end of a B♮ foot-joint is thus 663.62 millimeters from the cork. As mentioned on page 48, Boehm usually made the head-joint about 2 millimeters short at the tuning slide. This should be taken into account when measuring actual flutes.]

[In the system of fingering devised by Boehm, now in general use, the tone F♯ is obtained by pressing down with either the third, or second finger of the right hand, with the result that there is one closed hole below the open hole from which the tone F♯ is being emitted. This closed hole has the effect of slightly lowering the pitch of the tone. To compensate for this flattening the tone-hole for F♯ is usually placed a little above the position indicated in Table II. This displacement is about 1.2 millimeters, which gives 422.26 − 1.20=421.06 millimeters from the cork as the compensated position of the center of the F♯ hole.]

[In order to complete the dimensions of a flute, it is necessary to add data for the upper C♯ hole, and for the trill-key holes for D♮ and D♯. There is no formula for calculating these quantities. A study of ten selected Boehm & Mendler flutes gives the following dimensions:

	Diameter	Distance of center form cork
D♯ trill-key hole	7.6mm	216.30mm
D♮ trill-key hole	7.6	233.40
C♯ small tone-hole	6.6	253.50

Occasionally a flute is found with these small holes of a different diameter, and with corresponding changes in their positions; but the data given represent Boehm's later instruments.]

[The dimensions given in this section correspond to the pitch A=435, and for tone-holes 13.2 millimeters in diameter, having a maximum rise above the edge of the hole of about 3 millimeters; the data for any other pitch may be determined by the method described in the next section.]

III.   EXPLANATION OF THE SCHEMA

IN Table II there is given only one set of normal dimensions; since the normal pitch [now known as International or low pitch: A=435] is by no means in universal use, it is often necessary to have measurements corresponding to various given pitches, but the labor required to make the necessary calculations of dimensions involves much time and trouble.

These inconveniences have caused me to design a *Schema* in which the basis of all the calculations for measurements of length is graphically represented. In this diagram the geometrical proportions of the lengths of a string, corresponding to the reciprocals of the vibration numbers in the equally tempered scale, are represented by the intersections of horizontal and vertical lines; while diagonal lines indicate the geometrical progression in which the measures of length may be varied without disturbing their reciprocal proportions to the vibration numbers.

This graphic method was suggested by the plan of a monochord, on which, by means of a moveable bridge, the stretched string may be successively shortened to half of its original length, thereby producing all the intervals of one octave.

Now these proportions remain constant from the highest to the lowest musical tones, and the tran-

sition from one interval to the next can therefore
be represented graphically, and my *Schema* has
been founded upon these considerations. With
its help and without calculation, the centers of
the tone holes of all wind instruments constructed
on my system, as well as the positions of the so-
called frets of guitars, mandolins, zithers, etc.,
may be easily and quickly determined.

[The *Schema* seems to have developed gradually during Boehm's study of the dimensions of
the flute. The first definite reference to it is in
connection with the London Exhibition of 1862.
Mr. Wm. Pole reports (Welch, pp. 154, 157.) : "He
has sent for exhibition a geometrical diagram, with
explanations, by which makers of tubular instruments can, with the greatest readiness and accuracy, construct their instruments according to any
of the recognized pitches." Boehm later sent a
copy of the *Schema* to the Paris Exposition of 1867,
but the jury said they were not competent to decide upon the merits of a production which was
scientific rather than artistic. In a letter to Mr.
Broadwood, dated November 15, 1868, Boehm
says: "At the Paris Exposition, unfortunately,
the jurors, being unfamiliar with the subject, declined to go into it; wherefore, at the request of the
committee of the Bavarian Polytechnic Society,
I had my diagrams published in their *Kunst und
Gewerbeblatt.*" The account was given in the *Kunst
und Gewerbeblatt,* a periodical published in Munich, in October, 1868, and a copy of the original,
in German, is in the translator's collection. A

complete English translation of this description of the *Schema* has been given by Mr. Broadwood ("Essay on the Boehm Flute," pages 62-69). The explanation give by Boehm in "Die Flöte und das Flötenspiel," differs from that in the *Kunst und Gewerbeblatt* mainly in the omission of a figure showing details of the diagram; this figure has been reproduced in this edition as Fig. 12. A critical discussion of the *Schema,* as submitted to the Paris Exposition, has been given by M. Cavaillé-Coll (Welch, "History of the Boehm Flute," pages 306-313).]

My diagram, Fig. 12, consists of three parallel, horizontal lines of three different lengths, which start from a common vertical line, and are designated by *A, B,* and *C.* [In the original this diagram is given in half-size scale; it is here reproduced about one-fifth full size. In either case, for actual use, it would need to be redrawn accurately to full size. The dimensions shown on the diagram have been added by the translator, to make the construction plain; all of the dimensions are given in Table II. A portion of the *Schema,* drawn to full size, is shown in Fig. 13, on page 45.]

The central line represents the air column of a cylindrical flute tube, open at both ends, corresponding to the stretched string of the monochord, whose fundamental tone is C_3 of the scale founded on the normal pitch $A_3 = 435$ vibrations. The entire length of this air column, and therefore of the line *B,* for the fundamental tone C_3 is 670 millimeters. The sectional lengths for the tones of the

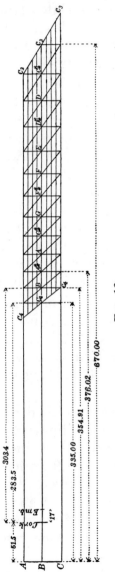

Fig. 12.

Schema for determining the positions of the tone-holes of wind Instruments at various pitches.

chromatic scale, calculated from the absolute vibration numbers for this pitch, and expressed in millimeters [see Table II], are given by the points of intersection of the line *B* with the vertical lines.

There is thus represented a standard of measurement, expressed in millimeters, to be taken from the upper end of the diagram along the line *B*. This diagram gives the actual dimensions of my flute, measured from the cork, if from each relative measure is subtracted the 51.5 millimeters (represented by the small cross line) which was previously added to complete the theoretical air column [see page 34]. More than this, all the data for calculation are present, if the absolute vibration numbers are written beneath the points of intersection of the length measures.

Since these standard measures correspond only to the normal pitch, it is necessary to be able to lengthen or shorten the relative distances of the tone-holes to correspond to varying pitches, with ease and without disturbing their reciprocal proportions.

This can be accomplished without computation by means of diagonal lines on the diagram which pass through the points of intersection of the vertical lines with the line *B*, both upwards and downwards to the points where the vertical lines end in the two parallel lines *A* and *C*. In this way are shown two new sets of measures, one corresponding to a pitch a half tone sharper, the other to one a half tone flatter.

[The construction may be carried out graphically as follows: After the several vertical lines have been drawn through the points of intersection on B, the line A is drawn parallel to B at any convenient distance; a diagonal line is drawn through each intersection of a vertical line with A to the intersection of the next lower vertical line with B, and is continued until it intersects the second lower vertical line below B; the line C is then determined by the last intersections of the diagonal and vertical lines.   If these intersections do not all fall on a straight line parallel to B, there has been a mistake in the construction of the diagram; as Boehm says, "the accuracy of the drawing is self-controlled."   Obviously, the ratio of the distances between the parallel lines A, B, and C, must be the same as that of the distances between any three successive vertical lines, which is the ratio of the semi-tone intervals of the equally tempered scale, 1.0595.   In Fig. 12, these distances have been taken equal to those between the vertical line for G and $F\sharp$, and $F\sharp$ and F, 26.59 millimeters and 28.17 millimeters, respectively. Any other pair of distances between tone-holes, would give a diagram with diagonal lines of a different slope, but all would lead to the same dimensions for the flute.]

A flute made to the shortened measurements of line A, will be exactly half a tone sharper than the normal pitch, while one made upon the longer dimensions of line C, will be exactly a half tone lower than the normal pitch.   Now as these diagonal lines may be looked upon as continuous series of tone-hole centers, which, in a geometrical progression, gradually approach each other above, and in the same way recede from each other below, it follows that the relative proportions of the distances of these points remain continually unchanged, wherever the diagonal lines are intersected by a new line parallel to the line *B*.

It is possible, therefore, as shown in the diagram, to draw six additional parallel lines between *A* and *C*, which, together with *B*, will give dimensions differing in pitch by one-eighth of a tone; and at will many other lines may be drawn, the intersections of each of which with the diagonal lines will give correct dimensions. The only remaining question is how such a line shall be drawn so that it shall correspond exactly to any given pitch.

In order to answer this question one must first express the pitch difference between the given pitch and the normal, in millimeters, which will give the difference between the length of the air column of the given tone, and the length for the same tone in normal pitch shown on line *B*. This will also determine the position of a new vertical section line crossing the line *B*, corresponding to the given tone.

If the desired pitch is higher than the normal, the vertical section line through the point on line *B*, corresponding to the new pitch, is to be extended upward toward *A*; while if the pitch is lower than the normal, the vertical line is to be extended downward toward *C*.

In either case the intersection of the vertical

line with a diagonal line is the point through which a new line parallel to *B* is to be drawn. The conversion of pitch difference into longitudinal measurement may be carried out as follows. The pitch to which an instrument is to be constructed may be given by a tuning fork, a tuning pipe, or by the number of vibrations, and in the *Schema* either an A or a C may be used.

For example, let there be given by a tuning fork an A_3 of 430 vibrations, which is 5 vibrations flatter than the normal A_3 of 435 vibrations, for which pitch the positions of all the tone-holes are required. In this case it is necessary merely to draw

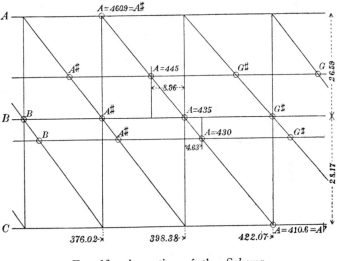

Fig. 13. A portion of the *Schema.*
Full size.

out the head joint of a normal flute until it is exactly in tune with the tuning fork (which naturally the ear determines) in which case the length drawn out will be found to be 4.63 millimeters. If, however, the given pitch is higher than the normal, for example $A_3=445$ vibrations, then, since the flute cannot be shortened, the head joint is to be drawn out till the tone B♭ is in unison with the A_3 of the fork. The length drawn out will be found to be 13.40 millimeters; and since the distance between the centers of the B_3♭ and A_3 holes of the normal flute is 22.36 millimeters, it follows that the air column corresponding to the A_3 of the fork is shorter than that of the normal flute by 8.96 millimeters.

If the pitch differences are given by vibration numbers, then the conversion into millimeter measures must be calculated. The vibration numbers are inversely proportional to the lengths; and the vibration numbers $A_3=430$ and $A_3=445$ are to the normal vibration number $A_3=435$, as the relative normal length 398.38 milimeters is to the required lengths. If now the numbers 435 and 398.38 are multiplied together, and the resulting product is divided by the numbers 430 and 445, the quotients are 403.01 and 389.42 which then represent the numbers of millimeters in the relative lengths, to which the vibration numbers have been converted. If these measurements correspond to the given vibration numbers 430 and 445, then the differences between them and the length of the normal A_3, 4.63 and 8.96 millimeters, must correspond to the vibration differences of 5 and 10 vibrations, respectively.

Therefore a vertical section line drawn through the line B at a point 4.63 millimeters distant from the center of the A_3 hole in the direction of A_3b, will correspond to $A_3=430$ vibrations; and a section line 8.96 millimeters distant from the A_3 hole in the direction of $A_3\sharp$ will correspond to $A_3 =445$ vibrations.

[In Boehm's original description of the *Schema* in the *Kunst und Gewerbeblatt,* a diagram accompanies the preceding explanation, which is omitted in "Die Flöte und das Flötenspiel." This drawing, given in Fig. 13, with some elaboration and with dimensions added, shows a portion of the *Schema* drawn accurately to full scale.]

The desired points of intersection will, in the manner mentioned above, be obtained from the diagonals leading upward or downward, and the results of this method of procedure will be found to be perfectly accurate.

Since the relative proportions of the vibration numbers and the measurements remain unchanged throughout the diagram, it is immaterial whether the given tone is an A, a C, or any other; and if the diagram is not sufficiently long for lower tones, it can be extended at will.

For each successive lower octave one has only to double all the dimensions; the accuracy of the drawing controls itself, for any error made would be at once evident by the drawing of the diagonal lines.

From this explanation it is evident that a flute can be in perfect tune at one pitch only, and that any shortening or lengthening of the tube above the tone-holes must work disadvantageously upon the intonation; in the first case the higher tones as compared with the lower are too sharp, and in the second case [drawing the tuning side], on the contrary, the lower tones are too sharp as compared with the higher.

Obviously, these difficulties are no more overcome by a longer or shorter head-joint, than by a simple drawing of the slide; this drawing-out must not be more than two millimeters. Small differences of pitch can, indeed, be compensated, so far as the ear is concerned, by a good embouchure. Accordingly I make the head-joints of my flutes about two millimeters shorter than is required for perfect tuning, so that one may not only draw out the head to lower the pitch, but that he may also make it somewhat sharper. However, it is best in ordering a flute to specify the pitch as accurately as possible, and at the same time to mention whether the player directs his embouchure inward or outward, as this also produces a considerable effect on the pitch.

[A study of eleven specimens verifies the statement made above. Four of these head-joints are exactly two millimeters short; two of them are three millimeters short. The average amount of shortening is 2.4 millimeters. Unfortunately the variation in pitch within the last fifty years has led many owners of Boehm's flutes to have them purposely altered; and often there are repairs to the head, or slide-joint, which alter the length. No instrument has ever been found which differs from the specified dimensions, which does not also show evidence of having been altered.]

[There has been a great deal of discussion as to the validity and utility of the *Schema*. It has been stated that Boehm himself did not follow the *Schema;* that flute makers in general do not use it; that a flute made according to the *Schema* would be so badly out of tune as to be unusable. (Rockstro, "The Flute," p. 169; Welch, "History of the Boehm Flute," p. 297). Much study has been given to the design of the scale of the flute, involving the accurate measurement of several hundred specimens, among which have been, perhaps, fifty made by Boehm. These flutes by Boehm represent all stages of his work from the year 1850 to 1880, and are of all sizes; there are bass flutes in G, military flutes in D♭, orchestra flutes of various pitches, and several with B♮ foot-joints. Every flute from Boehm's shops so far examined has been constructed accurately upon the dimensions explained in connection with the *Schema*. There is little need for argument regarding the tuning of these instruments: for fifty years many of the most eminent artists have used Boehm's flutes in some of the finest orchestras of the world, where the requirements of accurate tuning are the most exacting. At the time of writing (1921) the translator is using a Boehm & Mendler silver flute, made according to the *Schema* for the pitch $A = 435$. This has been played in direct comparison with several other instruments of the very highest quality recently made by the most eminent makers in America and abroad; and also in comparison with a flute constructed upon the translator's own improved (?) scale. Each flute has its individual characteristics, but in general Boehm's *Schema* is fully justified.]

[The *Schema* is certainly based upon rational principles, that is, it is "scientific;" it consists of the application of the laws of the musical scale to quantitive measurements. The fundamental interval of the octave is found only by experiment, and Boehm's value is the result of his years of experience. Any change in the diameter of the bore, in the size of the blow-hole, in the size of the tone-holes, in the length of the tube around the holes; any change in the rise of the keys, in the hardness of the pads, in the diameter of the metal washer holding the pads in place; any change in the manner of blowing, or even in the physical condition of the player himself—any of these changes would alter the fundamental interval and lead to a set of dimensions different from those given by Boehm. Nevertheless, the *Schema* is quite correct for a flute played as Boehm intended it to be played. Many performers wish modifications to favor or correct certain tones, or to suit their personal idiosyncrasies, and makers have adopted such changes, thus departing in detail from Boehm's measures. Such a change may be acceptable to one player and not to another; in any case they do not invalidate the *Schema*. In examining old flutes account must be taken of possible alterations. For instance the Heindl Flute, No. 19, (page 99) has the tone-holes spaced according to the *Schema* for the scale of A=445,

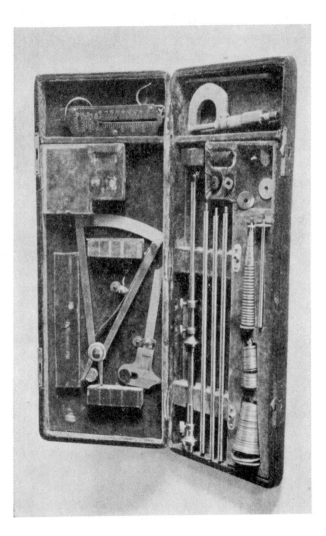

F<small>IG</small>. 14.

A set of instruments designed especially for measuring flutes

but the slide-joint has been shortened by 8 millimeters, raising the pitch to A=452. Evidence of this change is very plain when looked for.]

[A set of instruments for the accurate and convenient measurement of flutes, is shown in Fig. 14. With the exception of three pieces these tools were especially made for this purpose. There is a special caliper for measuring the diameters of the tone-holes without removing the keys; a jointed measuring rod, 1000 millimeters long, with vernier and with a special compensation, adjustable to any flute so that all measurements of length are referred to the center of the embouchure; a set of 170 standard disks for diameters of bore and of holes, differing by tenths of a millimeter (0.004 inch); a caliper for inside, outside, and depth measures; a standard micrometer caliper; and a delicate spring balance for weighing the parts.]

IV. THE MATERIAL

THAT the tones of a flute may not only be easily produced, but shall also possess a brilliant and sonorous quality, it is necessary that the molecules of the flute tube shall be set into vibration at the same time as the air column, and that these shall, as it were, mutually assist one another. The material must possess this requisite vibration ability, which is either a natural property of the body, for example as in bell-metal, glass and various kinds of wood, or has been artificially produced, as in the case of hardened steel springs and hard-drawn metal wire. [Undoubtedly the material of which a wind instrument is made sometimes affects the tone quality, but the manner in which this influence is exerted has not been explained; it is doubtful whether it is correct to ascribe it to the molecular vibrations of the material.]

Now in both cases the excitation of the vibrations requires the expenditure of energy proportional to the mass of the material. Consequently the tones of a flute will be more easily produced and the development of their full strength will require less effort in blowing, the less the weight of the flute tube.

Upon a silver flute, therefore, the thin and hard drawn tube of which weighs only **129 grams, the** brightest and fullest tone can be brought out and maintained much longer without fatiguing blowing, than can be done on a wood flute, which even when made as thin as possible still has double the weight, namely 227½ grams. [The silver tubes used by Boehm have a thickness of about 0.28 millimeters and the wooden tubes are 3.7 millimeters thick. The silver flute complete weighs about 330 grams and the wooden flute about 440 grams.]

Any variation in the hardness or brittleness of the material has a very great effect upon the timbre or quality of tone. Upon this point much experience is at hand, for flutes have been made of various kinds of wood, of ivory, crystal-glass, porcelain, rubber, papier-mâché, and even of wax, and in every conceivable way to secure the various desired results. Heretofore all of these researches have led back to the selection of very hard wood, until I succeeded in making flutes of silver and German silver, which now for twenty years have rivaled the wood flute. [Silver flutes were first introduced by Boehm in 1847.] Notwithstanding this it is not possible to give a decisive answer to the question "Which is the best?"

The silver flute is preferable for playing in very large rooms because of its great ability for tone modulation, and for the unsurpassed brilliancy and sonorousness of its tone. But on account of its unusually easy tone-production, very often it is overblown, causing the tone to become hard and shrill; hence its advantages are fully realized only through a very good embouchure and diligent tone-practice. For this reason wooden flutes on my system are also made, which are better adapted to the embouchures of most flute players; and the wood flutes possess a full and pleasant quality of tone, which is valued especially in Germany.

The silver flutes are made of a $\frac{9}{10}$ fine alloy [United States coin silver is $\frac{9}{10}$ fine; sterling silver is $\frac{925}{1000}$ fine]; and for the manufacture of wood flutes I usually employ either the so-called cocus wood, or the grenadilla wood of South America. The first, of dark or red-brown color, is especially desirable because of its brilliant tone, notwithstanding that this wood contains a resin, which, in very rare cases, induces an inflammation of the skin of the lip. To obviate this difficulty, as well as to secure a very pleasant ringing quality of tone in the high notes, many will prefer black grenadilla wood. Ebony and boxwood are now used only for the cheaper grades of instruments.

In the construction of my flutes only selected wood of the finest quality is used, and if a piece develops a defect during the working, it is at once cast aside, that no more time and labor may be lost.

However, a flute which is entirely free from defects may become cracked by improper handling, against which no guarantee is possible. Both the cause and the means of preventing such accidents should be understood, and I will therefore return to this subject later, under the heading, Treatment of the Flute in General.

[Boehm frequently combined two materials, making the body of silver and the head of wood. It was in his later years that he most strongly advocated this combination, though he had constructed such flutes in his earlier years, certainly as early as 1865. Three such instruments are shown in Figs. 7, 32, and 41; the latter two have heads of "thinned" wood. Notwithstanding Boehm's recommendation, such composite instruments have not grown in favor.]

Yours most truly

Theobald Boehm.

V. THE SYSTEM OF FINGERING

(a) General Description

HAVING determined the dimensions and material best suited for the flute tube, it was then necessary to devise a system of fingering by which all scales, passages, and trills in the twenty-four keys could be played, clearly, certainly, and with the greatest possible ease. [The chronological order is not accurately stated, for the system of fingering was practically completed in 1832, while the dimensions and material, as described above, were altered by the introduction, in 1847, of the silver flute with cylinder bore.]

This task I endeavored to accomplish in the following manner. Since the fifteen tone-holes of my flute tube could not be covered by means of the fingers, because the holes were too large and in some instances too far apart, it was necessary to furnish them all with keys which had then to be so arranged that they could be opened or closed at will.

For this purpose but nine fingers are available, since the thumb of the right hand is indispensable for holding the flute. The deficiency in fingers must therefore be made up by mechanism, whose systematic coupling makes it possible to close several keys at the same time with one finger. I have accomplished this by means of moveable axles, to which some of the keys are rigidly fastened, and on which other keys are merely hinged; by means of clutches underneath, the latter may be made to act upon the axles.

These axles may be lengthened as desired, so that the attached keys are manipulated at points within easy reach of the fingers; the means for accomplishing this had to be sought in the design of the key mechanism. After mature consideration of all the possible tone combinations and finger movements I made many sketches of mechanisms, in my effort to find the best methods of key connections. In such matters only actual trial can determine which is best. I constructed flutes on three entirely different models and after careful trial of all the advantages and disadvantages, that model of my flute which has since become well known proved itself in all respects the most suitable.

I have retained the three foot keys for $C_3\sharp$, D_3, $D_3\sharp$, for the little finger of the right hand, in the form already well established. The two trill keys for D_4 and $D_4\sharp$ are brought into use only for the highest tones $B_5\flat$ and B_5. Hence the number of keys to be arranged for in the regular scheme of fingering is reduced from fifteen to ten for the playing of which there are still eight fingers available.

There then arose the question, "Which method of construction, that with open keys or that with closed keys, is the most practicable?"

I chose the open keys, as giving the greatest

possible ease in playing, since they easily follow the movement of the fingers, and only weak springs are required to raise them quickly. On the contrary, closed keys require strong springs in order that large holes may be stopped airtight, and their motions are contrary to those of the fingers, [that is, when the finger is pressed downward the key over the hole moves upward].

After the ten holes from E to C♯ were provided with separate, easily moving keys, the eight fingers were placed upon them in the most practical arrangement which permitted the holding of the flute in a natural manner; then as many keys were closed as could be done with entire convenience; there remained open only the two holes for G and B [which, when closed, give F♯ and B♭], and for the closing of these the lack of fingers must be made up by mechanical contrivances.

For this two key combinations were necessary, namely the clutches for connecting the E, F, and F♯ keys with the lengthened moveable axle of the G key, and the clutches of the B♭ and the F♯ keys connecting with the axle of the B key.

As is shown in the following drawing (Fig. 20), the two keys G and B may be closed by means of the connected keys, without changing the lay of the fingers, and when the fingers are lifted the keys open of themselves by means of their own springs; thus one can play them at will.

In this way the very troublesome sliding from keys and tone-holes which is required on the old flute is entirely done away with, and one can certainly and easily play all possible tone combinations from low D_3 to high A_5. In my system each scale requires the use of all the fingers, and consequently they are all equally exercised, thus a player is in a condition to play in all keys with equal accuracy, certainty and ease.

In the following table of fingerings [page 72], those designated "irregular" may be used not only for facilitating certain passages, but they may also be employed in many cases for enharmonic differences, such as between F♯ and G♭.

The practicability of my system of fingering has long demonstrated itself not only in its use by artists, but also by beginning students who learn to play the scales and trills in all keys in much shorter time than was possible on the old flute.

The changing from the old flute to the new is not nearly so difficult as most players imagine. Ordinarily it requires only about two weeks for one to become familiar with the mechanism and the table of fingerings; and one will find compensation for the trouble involved in the clear, smooth and easy production of the tones.

(b) THE G♯ KEY

In the planning of my system of fingering, I made the G♯ key to stand open, like all the rest, only after mature consideration of all the advantages and disadvantages in acoustical, mechanical, and technical respects. The open key is advantageous because its motion is the same as that of the little finger of the left hand, and because of the weak spring required, its "play" is very light and convenient.

Since the unlearning of the former fingering appears to be a great difficulty to many [who would change from the ordinary flute to the new], artists and instrument makers have endeavored to adapt the fingering of the old flute, either wholly or in part, to my flute tube. For this reason there has been made in Paris, for many years, an alteration of my open G♯ key, which makes it like the closed G♯ key in its action. The use of this has spread somewhat, since it accommodates players of the old flute who can thus retain the former fingerings for G and G♯.

[The earliest type of G♯ key, first applied to the old system flute about 1775, is a simple key which is normally kept closed by a spring; this key is opened by the little finger of the left hand to produce the tone G♯. Boehm's system of 1832 required open keys and he devised the equally simple "Open G♯ Key." The earliest form of this key is shown in Fig. 4. After the invention of the cylinder bore and large, covered keys, in 1847, the key was given the form shown in Fig. 7, the A and G♯ keys being hinged on a short rod on the left (outer) side of the tube. Later all of the mechanism was attached to the inner side of the tube and the G♯ key took its present form as shown in Fig. 16. The A and G♯ keys are independently hinged on a short rod and each is an open-standing key. The third finger of the left hand plays directly on the A key and when the key is closed the tone

G♯ is produced. When the little finger of the left hand is pressed on the lever attached to the G♯ key this key is closed, making the tone G♮. The little finger must continue to close this key for the lower tones, F♯, F, E, etc. With the open G♯ key the little finger is in action to close the key for twenty-one notes of the thirty-nine notes which make the compass of the regular scale. With the closed G♯ key the little finger is required to open the key for five notes out of the thirty-nine notes in the scale. This more frequent use of the little finger, however, is so simple and logical and so directly in accord with the movements of the other fingers, that the open G♯ system, when once acquired, is quite as easy as any other.]

[Coche, of Paris, a teacher of the flute, brought out in 1838 the "Coche Perfected Model" which he announced as an improvement upon the Boehm system. One of the "improvements" was the adoption of a new type of closed G♯ key, devised about this time by Dorus, another flutist of Paris. A conical-bore flute by Godfroy, shown in Fig. 6, is provided with a Dorus G♯ key of the early form. This type of key as applied to the cylinder-bore flute of later type is shown in Fig. 17, as made by Louis Lot, and Fig. 15 is a diagram illustrating its operation. There is but one G♯ tone-hole which is opened and closed automatically with the A hole. When the A hole is closed, and with it the G♯ hole, the latter may be independently opened by pressing upon the G♯ lever with the little finger of the left hand. There is a lug, *l,* attached to the hinge tube of the A key which extends under the stem of the G♯ key; a strong spring, s_1, attached to the G♯ key rests against the under side of the lug so that the two keys move together, while, normally, both are held open by the weak spring, s_2. The adjustment of the key is such that when the A key is pressed to close its hole, the G♯ key touches the flute first; a slight further pressure of the A key closes the A hole and carries the

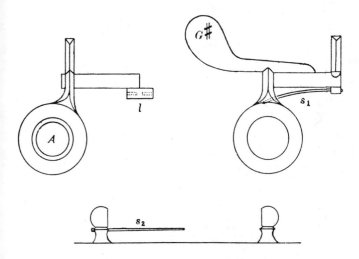

Fig. 15. The Dorus Closed G♯ Key.

lug below the stem of the G♯ key so that the strong spring, s_1, firmly closes the G♯ hole. While the A key is held closed by the third finger, and the G♯ key is closed by the spring, the little finger may be pressed upon the G♯ lever and thus open the G♯ hole, producing the tone G♯ as in the old system. When the little finger is raised the G♯ key closes, making G♮; when the third finger is raised both keys rise together through the action of the lug and the tone A is produced. This type of key operates satisfactorily on a flute with conical bore and small tone-holes, but on a flute of cylinder-bore and large holes the proper closing of the key is more difficult. The Dorus construction requires the location of the posts and hinge-tubes on the outer side of the flute.]

[The operation of the Dorus G♯ key is not always satisfactory and the necessity of placing the posts and axles of the keys on the outer side of the tube is particularly objectionable on flutes with cylindrical bore and large tone-holes. The Dorus key has largely been displaced by the duplicate-hole, closed G♯ key, Fig. 18, now in very general use. The G♯ tone-hole is placed on the inner side of the flute tube and is covered with a closed key, the manipulation of which is like that of the old system. In order that there may be no closed holes below the one from which the tone is being emitted, a duplicate G♯ tone-hole is used, located as in Boehm's construction; this is closed by a key rigidly attached to the A key; thus the duplicate hole opens and closes with the A hole, and G♯ is produced by pressing on the G♯ key. For certain tones it is desirable to close the G♯ hole while the A hole remains open. This is not possible with the closed G♯ key.]

[Boehm is said to have declined to make flutes with the closed G♯ key. However, he did in a few instances provide such instruments for players of the old flute. The translator has never

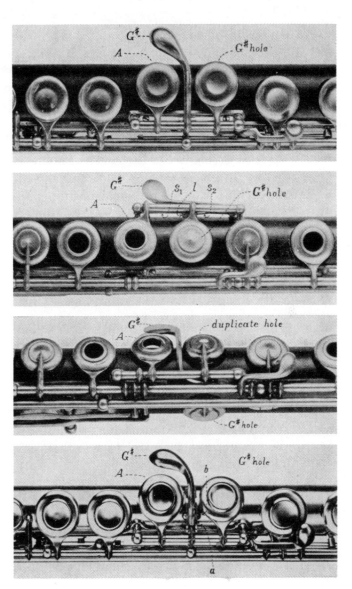

FIGS. 16, 17, 18, 19.
Open and closed G♯ keys

seen but one closed G♯ key made in Boehm's shop; nearly all the closed keys found on these flutes have been added by other makers. The one exception is the Macauley flute shown in Fig. 34. The closed key proper is exactly like Boehm's open G♯ key excepting that the spring is made strong and is so bent that it keeps the key closed. The lever is cut in two a little way from the axle as shown at *a*, Fig. 19, and the finger piece is then pivoted on a fulcrum, *b*, held in a silver guide attached to the tube. This key is played exactly as is the ordinary closed G♯ key; it can be opened and closed independently of the A key; thus it obviates the objections which Boehm urges against the other forms of closed key. Inasmuch as this key is normally closed, it would tend to flatten the tone A, just as the tone F♯ is flattened by the closing of a lower tone-hole. Boehm has corrected this effect upon the tone A by placing the A hole 1.2 millimeters above its *Schema* position, just as he and other makers correct the F♯ tone-hole. This plan of Boehm's is probably the simplest and perhaps the best form of closed G♯ key which has yet been made.]

[Various other schemes for a closed G♯ key have been devised but they are more or less complicated and have not found general acceptance. Boehm's arguments regarding the advantages of the open-key system are given in the following paragraphs.]

A combination of a closed G♯ key with an open A key would cause not only an entirely unnecessary complication in the key mechanism, and be a disadvantage from an acoustical aspect, but it would at the same time increase the difficulties of playing.

In order that a closed G♯ key may stop the large tone-hole air tight it must be provided with a strong spring, and it follows that the opening of the same requires a correspondingly greater force in the little finger of the left hand, than the pressing down of an open key which is held up only by a weak spring. But of still greater importance is the strength required in the third or ring finger in closing the A key, since this finger must overcome not only the spring required quickly to raise both of the combined keys, but at the same time it must overcome the strong closing-spring of the G♯ key. [The last sentence applies only to the Dorus G♯ key.]

It is easily seen that there is thus a loss in facility of playing in general, and, further, that all trills with these keys, and especially the trill G♯ with A, become much more difficult, than with the easy-moving, open-standing keys. Moreover, in the frequent combinations of the tones G♯ or A♭ with the lower tones F♯, F, E, E♭, and D, the little finger of the left hand must move in a direction contrary to that in which the fingers of the right hand are moving at the same time. That it is easier to make similar motions with the fingers of both hands simultaneously, rather than contrary motions, and therefore that playing with a closed G♯ key is the more difficult, no one will deny.

Yet there is another difficulty from an acoustical aspect. Because of the connection of the G♯ key with the A key, the A hole cannot be opened by itself, the G♯ hole being always open at the same time; this causes the E_5 to be too sharp, and its production is interfered with. The production of this tone is a little more certain, when the G♯ hole remains closed; and in rapid alternations, also in delicate slurring together of the E_5 with other tones such as G_4♯, A_4, A_5, A_3, etc., the advantage is very perceptible.

Finally, this complication of the mechanism [for any type of closed G♯ key] is wholly superfluous, since each one of these two keys has its own proper finger, and each can be easily opened or closed in the most natural and simplest way in my system. The above mentioned difficulties appear to have long been apparent in Paris, since a special lever has been added so that the difficult trills may be made with the strong first finger of the right hand.

And yet again a second G♯ hole has sometimes been bored in the flute tube and provided with an independent G♯ key. In both of these cases the mechanism is rendered still more complicated. I have no objection to make, if amateurs, with little time or zeal for practice, and who will be satisfied with playing in a few keys only, when changing from the old flute to the new, believe they will find the closed G♯ key the easier; yet

I hold that it is wrong to instruct beginners in
this way, since they will learn to play in all keys
more easily, and consequently more quickly, by
following my system as finally perfected.

[Rockstro, in his "Treatise on the Flute," pages
191, 359, and 389, argues eloquently and at length
in favor of the open G♯ key; he says: "Not many
years ago some opposition was raised to the
frequent use of the left thumb on the flute. We
do not now hear much of this * * * but there is
still rife, in some quarters, a strong prejudice
against the use of the little finger of the same
hand * * *. No one has ever objected to the
continued use of the right little finger * * *.
Theobald Boehm deserved much credit for his
courageous and persistent efforts to bring this
finger into activity. * * *"]

[The translator first learned to play a flute of
the old-system and then for ten years he used a
Boehm system flute with closed G♯ key; later
several flutes with open G♯ keys were added to his
collection and for the last twenty years he has
played mostly upon these. After many years of
experience, during which excellent flutes of all
three types of G♯ keys were constantly in his possession, and after the most careful and long continued trials, he is firmly convinced that Boehm's
arguments are fully justified. The advantages of
the open G♯ key are largely mechanical, and may
not be sufficient to justify an established performer
in changing, but they are such that every beginner
and everyone changing from the old to the Boehm
system, should choose the open G♯ key.]

VI. TABLES OF FINGERINGS

REGULAR FINGERINGS
OF THE CHROMATIC SCALE
FOR THE NEWLY CONSTRUCTED FLUTE OF
THEOBALD BOEHM

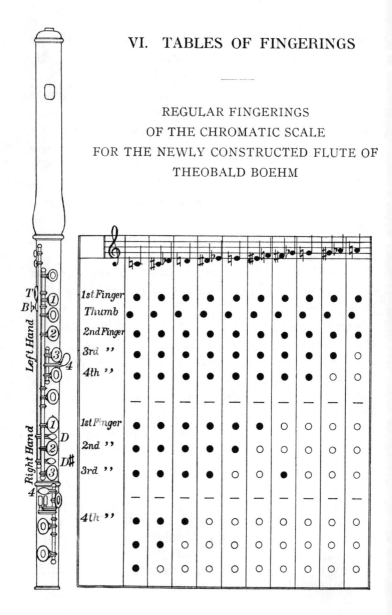

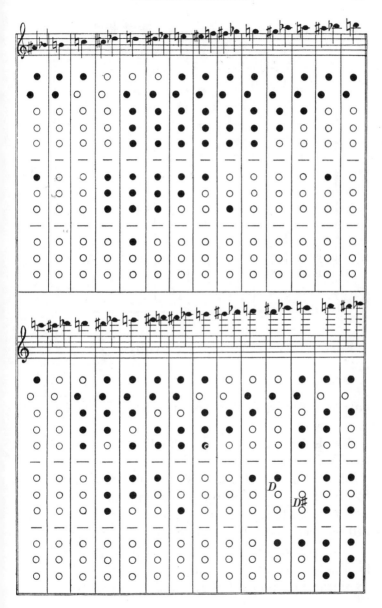

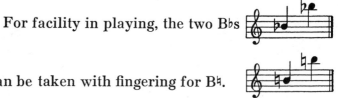

For facility in playing, the two B♭s

can be taken with fingering for B♮.

if the B key is closed by the thumb pressing on the B♭ lever.

The irregular fingerings may be used not only for facilitating certain passages, but also they may be made valuable in many cases for enharmonic differences, such as between F♯ and G♭.

[The use of the octave-key on the ordinary flute is the same as with the bass flute, which is explained on pages 128 and 129; see also page 86.]

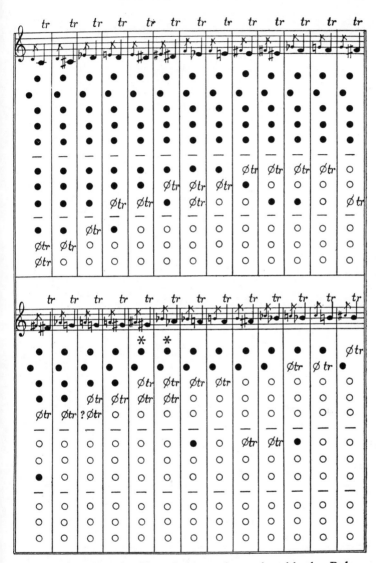

The trills marked with a * are to be made with the B key closed by the thumb lever. [The ? indicates that the trilling of the corresponding hole is optional.]

The trills marked with a * are to be made with the B key closed by the thumb lever. [The ? indicates that the trilling of the corresponding hole is optional.]

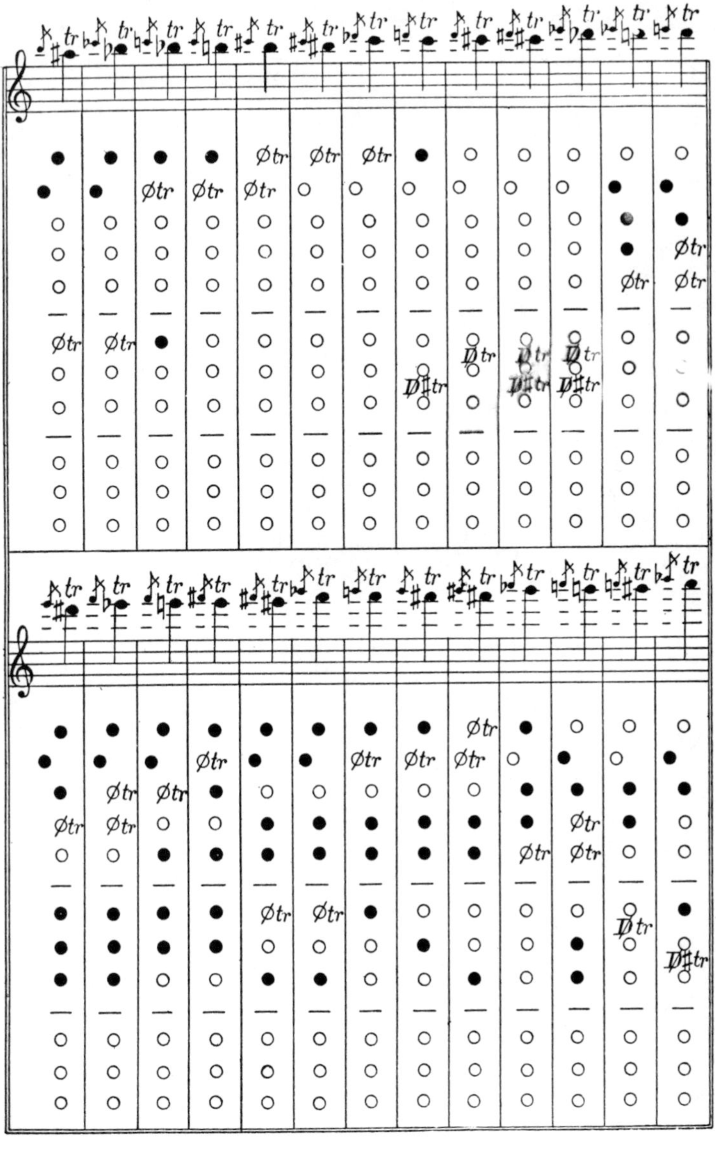

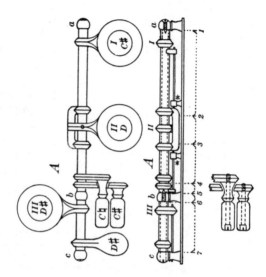

Fig. 20. Key Mechanism.

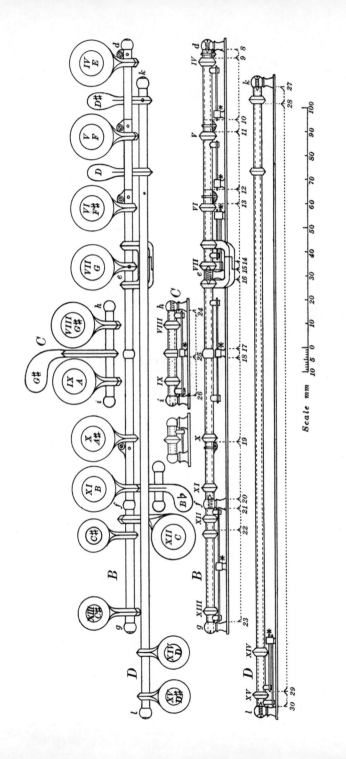

Scale mm

VII. DESCRIPTION OF THE KEY MECHANISM

IN order to give a clear idea and explanation of the key mechanism of my flute, I have represented it in full size,* Fig. 20, projected on a plane, and below I have shown a side view of the inner parts which are not visible to the eye.

In the latter view metal strips are shown, which in the metal flute are soldered to the body, and in the wooden flute are screwed on, forming the supporting points for the mechanism. Below these strips, and exactly corresponding with the drawing above, are dotted lines and figures which indicate all the joints of the mechanism, and the dimensions of the axles of the separate keys and clutches.

The key mechanism is divided into four groups which are designated in Fig. 20 by *A, B, C,* and *D.* Fig. 21 is a cross section of one key, Fig. 22 is a

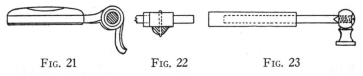

FIG. 21   FIG. 22   FIG. 23

Details of Key Mechanism.

clutch with its pin, and Fig. 23 represents one of the movable hinge tubes slipped off from its axle.

We will first explain the mechanism of the key-group *A* of the drawing.

* In this Dover edition, Figure 20 is reproduced at a reduction of approximately 35 per cent.

In the upper line the foot keys I, II, and III are represented, and in the side view beneath, the separate joints of the mechanism are shown, the lengths of which are indicated by the perpendicular dotted lines below the metal strip, designated by the figures 1 to 7.

The three pillars with spherical heads, *a, b, c,* which form the supporting points of the mechanism, are united to the metal strip and soldered, while the strip is soldered or screwed onto the foot joint.

Pointed screws are threaded in the spheres *a* and *b,* forming the pivots on which turns a steel axle (from 1 to 5) the ends of which have conical holes.

The C♯ key, I, turns upon this axle; this key is soldered to the hinge tube 1 to 2, and by means of a loop it connects with the hinge 3 to 4 which carries the lever arm (C♮ lever), all being joined into one continuous piece. The D key II is likewise soldered to a hinge (2 to 3) and being placed inside of the loop, the two keys are slipped over the axle; the key II is then made fast to the axle by a small pin passing through both. On the upper end of the axle (at 4 to 5) a lever arm is soldered, so that the axle and the D key move with it. These two keys are provided with springs which hold them open, and with rollers screwed onto the lever arms at right angles; by pressing on the rollers one can at will close one key, or through their coupling at the loop, both may be closed together.

The closed D♯ key III is provided with a strong spring, and moves on an axle, screwed into the sphere *b;* the sharpened end of this axle (at 5) forms the pivot of the movable axle of the lower keys.

The springs for the keys I and II are firmly inserted in the little posts marked thus, *, and push against the hinges by means of small blocks which are soldered fast; the spring for key III is fastened in the spherical pillar *c*.

The key-group *B* contains two moveable axles from 8 to 15 and from 16 to 20. The G key VII is soldered to the axle, at 14 and 15, which turns on the pivots of the pillars *d* and *e*. Next to this key is the hinge tube 13-14 to which the F♯ key VI and a half of the loop clutch is soldered.

The other half of the loop is fastened to the second moveable axle, and since the two half-loops touch one another, the two moveable axles may be coupled together.

This F♯ key is played by the first or index finger of the right hand.

Next to this is the small hinge piece 12-13, which is fastened to the steel axle by means of a small pin. On this hinge piece there is soldered a side wing, against which presses an adjustable screw attached to the shank of key VI. This screw must be so adjusted that when pressing down the F♯ key VI the steel axle is turned and through this the attached key G VII is closed.

If now the two other keys F V and E IV, which are played by the second and third fingers, are mounted in exactly the same fashion and are each coupled with the steel axle, then by pressing down either of these keys, separately or together, the G key VII will be closed each time [producing the tone F♯]; thus four keys and consequently four tone-holes can be opened or closed at will by three fingers. It is by this contrivance that one of the lacking fingers is replaced. [The arrangement, however, is not perfect, for the hole next below that from which the tone is being emitted is closed. This lowers the pitch perceptibly and muffles the tone very slightly. A partial compensation is obtained by placing the tone-hole for F♯ slightly above its true position, as explained on page 37.]

We come now to the upper half of this group.

Upon the steel axle which turns between the two pivots at 16 and 20 there is soldered a hinge, which extends from 16 to 18 and upon which at 16 there is the half loop for coupling with the lower steel axle, and at 17 and 18 is attached a sphere which serves as an ornament.

The A♯ key X is soldered to the hinge tube 18-19, and placed next to this sphere. This key is played by the middle finger of the left hand, and by means of its adjusting screw presses upon the wing of the hinge 19-20, through which the B key XI is closed.

Since the B key XI is connected to the steel axle by a pin near 19, and is coupled at 19 with the A♯ key X by the clutch, and at the same time it is coupled with the lower steel axle by the loop at 14-15, this key is itself closed by each pressing of the A♯ key X and also by pressing the F♯ key VI. It is clear that by these couplings still another finger is replaced, and consequently by means of this mechanism [together with that described in the next two paragraphs] six keys can be played entirely at will by four fingers [and the thumb].

Into the upper side of the spherical pillar *f* is screwed an axle, the point of which forms the pivot at 20. Moving on this axle are the two keys C XII and C♯ XIII. The first is soldered to the hinge tube 21-22 and is played by the thumb of the left hand. The second key C♯ XIII, and its lever are soldered to the hinge tube 22-23; the key played by the first or index finger of the left hand acting on the lever.

The group *C* consists of two separate keys, which move on the axle screwed into the spherical pillar *h*. The G♯ key VIII and its lever, upon which presses the fourth or little finger of the left hand, are soldered to the hinge 24-25. The A key IX which is played by the third finger, is soldered to the hinge tube 25-26.

The group *D* likewise contains only two keys, namely the two trill keys for D and D♯. The D♯ key XV and its spring hook are soldered to the hinge tube 29-30, and this tube in turn is soldered to the upper end of the long steel axle which turns on the pivots of the two spherical pillars *k* and *l*. On the lower end of this axle is the short piece of tube 27-28, which is connected with the axle by a pin; soldered to this tube is the D♯ lever which is played by the third finger of the right hand.

Between these two pieces is placed a long hinge tube which reaches from 28 to 29. Upon the upper end is soldered the D key XIV and at the lower end the corresponding D lever, which is played by the second finger. Both keys are provided with strong closing springs at 29 and 30.

Besides these keys there is still to be provided a B♭ lever next to the C key XII, which can be pressed with the thumb of the left hand, at the same time that the C key is closed, thus closing the B key XI also [and producing the tone B♭]. This lever is provided with its axle and spring, and serves in many cases to facilitate the playing.

Further, as the drawings show, all the springs, with the exception of that for closing the lower D♯ key III [and for the B♭ thumb lever], are fastened in the little pillars designated with an *; these springs press upon little hooks soldered to the hinge tubes, in such a way as to close the two trill keys D and D♯, and to hold all the other keys open.

These explanations correspond to all the styles of flutes made by the firm "Th. Boehm & Mendler in München."

[The original Boehm-system flute, including the models both of 1832 and of 1847, did not have a B♭ thumb lever. This attachment was devised by Briccialdi, an Italian flutist then resident in London, and was first applied to his own flute by Rudall and Rose in 1849. This lever, essentially in its original form, marked *B♭* in Figs. 24 and 26, is in very general use at the present time. Soon

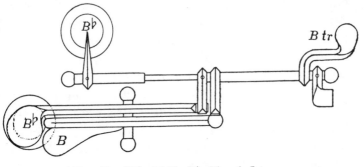

Fig. 24. Briccialdi's B♭ Thumb Levers.

after Briccialdi's invention, Boehm devised the B♭ thumb lever described in the preceding paragraph and marked *B♭*, in Figs. 25, 27 and 28.]

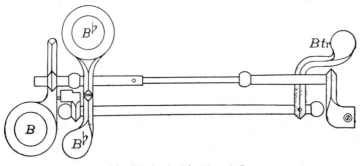

Fig. 25. Boehm's B♭ Thumb Levers.

[A lever for making the trill of B and C, *B tr* in Figs. 24, 25, 26 and 27, played with the first finger of the right hand, has been combined with each of these arrangements. Boehm seems never to have considered these levers as essential parts of his system, but rather as extra attachments; this is indicated by the fact that they are used only incidentally in the Tables of Fingerings. Boehm considered his own arrangement more rational than that of Briccialdi, since the thumb is placed on the key *B*, Figs. 25, 27 and 28, to produce the tone B, and to produce the next *lower* tone B♭, the thumb is moved *downwards* to the lever *B*♭. On the contrary, in Briccialdi's arrangement, the thumb is placed on *B*, Figs. 24 and 26, to produce the tone B, and to produce the *lower* tone B♭, the thumb is moved *upwards* to the lever B♭.]

[In addition to the mechanism described, Boehm recommended the "Schleifklappe," referred to in the original only in connection with the Bass Flute. The schleif-key, usually called the "octave-key" or the "whisper-key," is simply a small vent-key, which assists in the formation of a loop in the sound wave, or, what is of the same effect, it prevents the formation of a node at the place where the hole is located, thus giving freer speech and greater purity of tone. It is an adaptation of a similar octave-key which is required on all reed instruments, in which the formation of the over-tones is not as certain as on the flute. The octave-key is a small closed key, the touch of which is at *S*, Figs. 27 and 28, just above the thumb key; it is always played in connection with the thumb key and is easily opened by a slight rolling motion of the thumb. The hole for this key on a C flute is from 4.5 to 5.0 millimeters in diameter and is placed about 7 millimeters above the C♯ hole. The applications of the fingerings for the flute, in C are the same as for the bass flute, which are

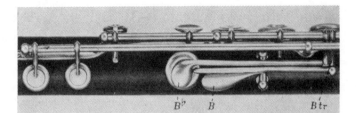

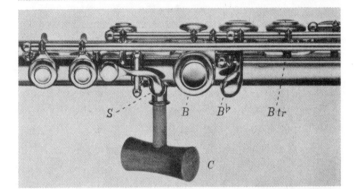

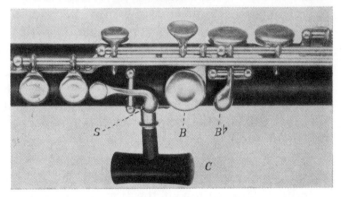

Figs. 26, 27, and 28.
Briccialdi and Boehm thumb keys

given in the supplementary tables of fingerings on page 129. Boehm writes in a letter dated November 8, 1873 (Broadwood, p. 59): "I find this little key very useful if the player wishes always to be in perfect tune in the following notes:

These tones always have a tendency to get a little flat if played *pianissimo,* while if you open the little octave-key they are not only perfectly correct, but also sound very easily."]

[In the translator's collection are several Boehm & Mendler flutes having the octave-key, one of them being the bass flute in G. After many trials extending over a period of years the conclusion is that, for several of the notes mentioned in the supplementary tables of fingerings, the influence of the key cannot even be detected, while for the other notes its effect is very small, so small as to be entirely negligible. This, no doubt, accounts for the fact that the octave key has not been generally adopted.]

[Fig. 29 is a plan, drawn full size, of the keys for a foot-joint to B♮, as often made by Boehm & Mendler. The action of the low B♮ key is carried around the C♮ and C♯ keys, and is pivoted on an extension of the axle which passes through the D♯ key. The other details are the same as explained for the C♮ foot-joint.]

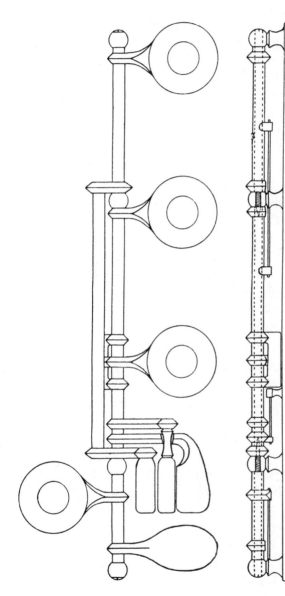

FIG. 29. Mechanism for foot-joint to B.

[The mechanism is substantially the same for flutes of both wood and silver. The walls of the tube of the wooden flute are 3.7 millimeters thick, and the silver tubes are about 0.3 millimeter thick. The "straps," or action plates to which the posts are attached are about 1.2 millimeters thick. The centers of the spherical heads of the action posts, that is the points of the pivot-screws, are about 6.1 millimeters above the plate for the main body and foot-joint keys of a wooden flute, and 6.9 millimeters high for trill keys. For a silver flute the pivots on the body joint are about 8.2 millimeters above the action plate, and on the foot-joint 6.2 millimeters above the action plate. The posts for the A and G♯ keys and for the thumb keys are shorter and vary somewhat in different specimens.]

[From 1812 to 1817 Boehm had a goldsmith's shop in which he constructed flutes on the old system. In 1828, he established his first real flute shop where he made improved old-system flutes and where he worked out the ideas for the Boehm System of fingering which were embodied in the first properly so-called Boehm flute of 1832. Very few flutes were made after 1832 and the shop was entirely given up in 1839. During this period the genuine Boehm flutes were made by Rudall and Rose in London and by Godfroy in Paris, under specific arrangements with Boehm. In 1847 Boehm announced the new flute with cylinder bore, metal body and covered keys, and he again established his own factory for the manufacture of flutes which continued in the same place for over fifty years. (See the appendix.) Patents were obtained in England and France covering the cylinder bore and the parabolic head-joint, and the above-mentioned firms were given licenses to make Boehm flutes. The flutes made in Boehm's own shops from 1847 to 1867 were marked "Th. Boehm in München," and bore serial numbers. In 1854 Carl Mendler, a watchmaker, became a workman in Boehm's shop. In 1862 he was made foreman and he was made a partner in 1867, the firm being known as "Th. Boehm & Mendler." The flutes were marked with the firm name in two styles, as shown in Fig. 30; silver flutes have the name engraved on the barrel of the slide-joint; wooden flutes are marked on a silver ferrule on the tenon of the slide-joint, which is usually covered by the socket on the head-joint. The name is not repeated on other parts of the flute. There are no serial numbers. After Boehm's death, in 1881, the business was carried on by Carl Mendler but the flutes continued to be marked Boehm & Mendler. Carl Mendler was succeeded by his son Carl Mendler, about 1895, who later gave up the manufacture of flutes.]

[Under Mendler's direction the flutes of Boehm & Mendler were constructed with workmanship of the most excellent quality, rarely equalled; they were beautifully designed, exquisitely finished, and their adjustment was perfect. The translator's historical collection of flutes contains, in January, 1922, about two hundred and fifty in-

FIGS. 30.
The Boehm & Mendler labels

struments of all types. Among them are sixteen specimens of various styles and scales from Boehm's own work-shop; these flutes are shown in the group picture, Fig. 31. Three particularly fine instruments, Nos. 13, 5 and 12, which were made for Rev. Rush R. Shippen, Mr. Carl Wehner, and General Daniel Macauley, respectively, are shown in larger size in Figs. 32, 33 and 34. The Heindl flute, No. 9, and the bass flute, No. 16, are shown in Figs. 7 and 41, respectively. These flutes, and also many others of Boehm's make, have been studied critically and have been measured in minute detail. These investigations have developed the greatest admiration for the painstaking care in the details of the scales, for the superb workmanship, and for the exquisite finish of these instruments. The Macauley flute (No. 12 in the group) fully exemplifies this praise. With the exception of the first instrument, which was never furnished with keys, and number nine, the Heindl flute, which has had excessive wear, these flutes are in good order; in fact, most of them are in as perfect condition as when new. The flutes 10, 12, 14 and 16 in the group, are much used for musical purposes, with perfect satisfaction. Some details regarding the several instruments are given in the following list:

No. 1—Flute in G. A=440. Boxwood. Tube of thinned wood with raised finger-holes, to which keys have never been attached. Given by Boehm to James S. Wilkins, Jr., in 1873, and presented to the translator by Mr. Wilkins in 1909.

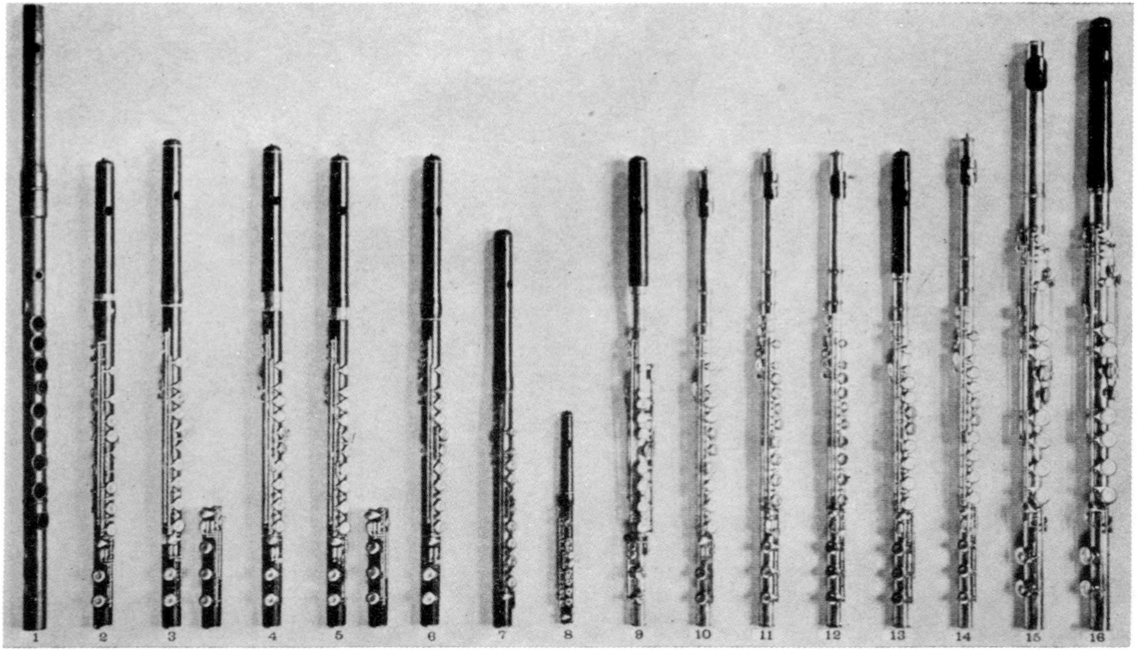

FIG. 31.

Boehm & Mendler Flutes in the Collection of Dayton C. Miller

No. 2—Flute in C. A=450. Grenadilla wood. Silver keys, gold springs. Mechanism of an unusual type, made by Boehm about 1860. Brought to America by Gustave Oeschsle, in 1864, who used it in the New York Academy of Music and in Gilmore's Band. It was later used by Mr. H. H. Honeyman.

No. 3—Flute in C. A=440. Grenadilla wood. Silver keys, gold springs. This flute was obtained from Boehm by Mr. Edward Martin Heindl. It was used by Mr. Frank Wadsworth, and later for eleven years by Mr. Louis Fritze, in Sousa's Band, and played in the "around-the-world" tour. The B♮ foot-joint was used by Mr. William Schade.

No. 4—Flute in C. A=435. Grenadilla wood. Silver keys, steel springs. History unknown.

No. 5—Flute in C. A=445. Cocus-wood. Silver keys, gold springs. With extra foot-joint to B♮. Belonged to Mr. Carl Wehner. Shown separately in Fig. 33.

No. 6—Flute in C. A=450. Cocus-wood. Silver keys, gold springs. With the octave key. With a duplicate-hole G♯ key, added by Wm. R. Meinell. History unknown.

No. 7—Flute in D♭. A=450. Grenadilla wood. Silver keys, gold springs. Foot to D♮.

No. 8—Piccolo in D♭. A=450. Grenadilla wood. Silver keys, steel springs. Cylinder bore. Used by Edward Martin Heindl.

No. 9—Flute in C. A=445. German Silver, silver plated. With graduated tone-holes. No. 19, made by Boehm about 1850. Brought to America in 1864 by Edward Martin Heindl, and used by him in the famous Mendelssohn Quintette Club, and in the Boston Symphony Orchestra upon its organization in 1881. This is probably the first metal Boehm flute to be brought to America. It is provided with both silver and wood heads. The mechanism on the middle joint has been partly rebuilt. This flute originally had no B♭ thumb key, and a special attachment for this was added by Mr. George W. Haynes in 1886, who also used the flute for a time. Shown separately in Fig. 7.

No. 10—Flute in C. A=438. Silver. Gold embouchure, steel springs. The trill lever for the right, first finger operates on the B♮ key on the upper side of the flute, instead of on the thumb key. This flute was played in Buffalo Bill's Wild West Show on its European Tour, and later was used by Mr. W. H. Guyon.

No. 11—Flute in C. A=448. Silver. Gold embouchure, gold springs, octave key, foot-joint to B♮. Made in 1877 for Mr. O. F. Chaffee of Detroit.

No. 12—Flute in C. A=445. Silver. Two sizes of tone-holes. Gold embouchure, gold springs, raised gold plates in center of each key, gold ferrules and tips; octave key, and special form of closed G♯ key (see page 68), ivory crutch. This superb flute is a remarkably beautiful specimen of flute workmanship, and it is in a perfect state of preservation. It was made in 1877, and was on exhibition in Berlin and in Paris for some time (probably in the Paris Exposition of 1878). It was made upon order for General Daniel Macauley, at one time Mayor of Indianapolis. The delivery of the flute was delayed nearly a year, while it was being exhibited. Boehm wrote, in sending the flute, that it was "the last flute I shall ever make and the best I have ever made; it is the 'last child of my life' with which I hate to part." Shown separately in Fig. 34.

No. 13—Flute in C. A=450. Silver. Bore 20 millimeters. Holes spaced to the scale A=455, but sounding A=450 because of the large bore. Two sizes of holes. Head of thinned wood, octave key, gold springs; foot-joint to B♮. Made in 1879 for Rev. Rush R. Shippen. Shown separately in Fig. 32.

No. 14—Flute in C. A=435. Silver. Gold embouchure, gold springs, octave key, foot-joint to B♮. This flute evidently was made about the year 1877. It is in as perfect condition as when new, and is used by the translator for musical purposes perhaps more than is any other instrument in his collection. While it may be equalled as to musical qualities by two or three

FIG. 32.
The Shippen Flute

FIG. 33.
The Wehner Flute

FIG. 34.
The Macauley Flute

modern instruments of the most celebrated makes, yet it is not surpassed by any, and the same may be said with respect to the beauty of design and perfection of workmanship of the instrument as a whole.

No. 15—Flute in G. A=443. Silver. Ebonite embouchure, octave key, steel springs.

No. 16—Flute in G. A=440. Silver. Thinned-wood head, octave key, steel springs. Used by Carl Wehner. Shown separately in Fig. 41. A more complete description with dimensions, is given in Chapter XII.]

[Statements have frequently been made by both makers and players of the flute that Boehm's own instruments were not accurate in scale and were not in accordance with his published descriptions. Such opinions are explicitly stated by Rockstro in his "Treatise on the Flute." This remarkable and otherwise excellent work is sadly marred by the author's intense prejudice against Boehm and by his efforts to belittle Boehm's contributions. Rockstro makes certain specific statements about Boehm's flutes which must be in error. He illustrates and describes a flute made by Boehm, (pages 374, 375, 390, 391) of which he says: "The diameter of the holes of a German silver flute that he made about the year 1851 vary, very irregularly from 0.46 inch (11.7 mm.) for the C_4 hole to 0.539 inch (13.7mm.) for $D_3^\sharp$ hole. The distances between the holes are also extremely irregular, so much so that I have not thought it worth while to give an account of them. The tone of this flute is very poor and thin, not nearly equal to that of an eight-keyed flute of average excellence." Nothwithstanding Rockstro's measures are given to the thousandth of an inch, yet it is believed that his general statement must be in error. In support of this opinion, and in justice to Boehm, certain even more specific statements of facts may be made regarding the Heindl flute, Boehm's No. 19 made about 1850, and illustrated as No. 9 in the group picture, and also in Fig. 7. No. 19 is apparently exactly like the flute illustrated in Rockstro's Treatise. No. 19 has graduated holes, the thumb-key hole is 11.4 millimeters in diameter, and the low C♯ hole is 13.6 millimeters in diameter. The holes increase in diameter, with perfect regularity from the smaller to the larger, each hole being exactly 0.2 millimeter larger than the preceeding one. The holes are spaced with perfect regularity, and exactly to the scale A=445, no hole deviating from the precise position required by Boehm's *Schema* by so much as half of a hundredth of an inch (there being the usual correction for the F♯ hole). The fact that Heindl used this flute for solo playing with the famous Mendelssohn Quintette Club and with the Boston Symphony Orchestra for many years is sufficient argument as to its quality of tone and correctness of tuning.]

VIII. CARE OF THE MECHANISM

(a) REPAIRS

E VEN though kept from violent injuries, the flute, like other mechanisms, will occasionally need repairs.

In practical use the keys move up and down a countless number of times, and all metal being subject to wear, the appearance of defects from this cause is unavoidable, even in the most solidly constructed mechanisms.

A spring may break or lose its elasticity; the oil, with which the axles and pivots must be covered, will become thick and sticky with time, and especially by the entering of dust, thus hindering the easy movement of the keys; or it may be necessary to replace an injured pad.

In all these cases it is necessary to remove the keys from the body and sometimes to take the mechanism to pieces. A person with some experience who has made himself familiar with the construction, and who is provided with the few tools which are required, will have no difficulty in doing this. Every flutist should be in a position, therefore, himself to undertake small repairs, and he should not trust his instrument to incapable hands.

(b) THE KEYS

The unscrewing and taking apart of the key mechanism may be performed in the manner described in the following paragraphs.

First, all of the springs, designated by a *, Fig. 20, in each key group in which one or more keys are to be taken away, must be unhooked. This may be accomplished by means of the little fork represented in Fig. 35, with which the outer ends

FIG. 35. Fork for setting springs.

of the springs can be pushed far enough backwards to disconnect them from the little hooks.

For removing the foot keys of group *A*, Fig. 20, turn the pointed screw *a* backwards so that the steel axle with the C♯ I and D II keys attached can be taken out. A screwdriver of the form shown in Fig. 36 is convenient for turning the screws.

FIG. 36. Screw Driver.

If the pin of the D key II, which projects a little below, be drawn out, both keys are loosened and can be pushed off the axle. [The translator would advise, unless there is urgent need, that these pins should not be removed. For the purposes of cleaning, it is sufficient to remove the several groups of keys from the body, and to clean these groups without separating them into single pieces.] By unscrewing the small steel axles on which the rollers turn, these may also be removed from the lever arms.

To remove the D♯ key III, unscrew the steel axle and draw it out of the hinge.

By unscrewing the pointed screw *d* the lower section 8 to 15 of group *B* may be taken off, and likewise the upper section 16 to 20 may be removed by unscrewing the upper steel axle which forms the pivot at 20. The keys can be slipped off the moveable steel axles as soon as the pins through the clutch joints are pushed out.

To remove the C key XII, partly draw out the steel axle which goes entirely through the C♯ key XIII.

In the group *C* the two keys G♯ VIII and A IX, in similar fashion, are taken off by withdrawing, partially or wholly, the steel axle which is screwed into the sphere *h*.

For the removal of the two trill keys D XIV and D♯ XV of group *D,* loosen the pointed screw in the spherical pillar *l.* The D key XIV as well as its hinge can be drawn off the steel axle as soon as the pin through the lever arm at 28 (D♯ lever) is pushed out.

When taking off and separating the key mechanism, it is best to lay each separate piece in its proper order on a sheet of paper; this will much facilitate the putting together, and it will not be so easy to interchange or lose anything. Each piece can then be readily cleaned and polished.

All the surfaces may be cleaned with a cloth or chamois skin, and the inside of the hinge tubes with a small feather or a tuft of cotton which may be pushed through the little tubes with a small stick of wood, etc. [or be drawn through with a fine copper wire].

After this cleaning the surfaces may best be polished with a piece of fine glove leather [chamois skin] and a fine polishing brush with the application of a little rouge, such as is used by jewelers.

When putting the mechanism together again, all the places at which rubbing occurs must be properly oiled. For this purpose watch oil is best, but one may also use neats-foot oil or perfectly pure olive oil which has stood in the sun for a time and thereby been purified by sedimentary precipitation.

The steel axles should be wiped with a little piece of cloth slightly wet with oil, and the pointed screws (pivots) are best oiled with the point of a wooden toothpick. One should not use more oil than is really necessary for the protection of the rubbing surfaces.

In putting together and screwing on the mechanism, as is self-evident, one must in each particular follow exactly the reverse order to that which was used in taking the instrument apart. It is necessary in each key group first to joint the pieces, after sliding them over the steel axles, by tightly inserting the pins; the separate groups of keys are screwed on, and finally the springs are hooked.

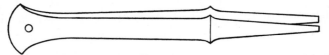

Fig. 37. Tweezers.

For holding the little screws, pins and springs, tweezers such as are shown in Fig. 37, are useful.

For cementing leather or cloth [or cork] linings which have fallen off the keys, etc., a proper solution of shellac in alcohol serves best.

(c) The Key Pads

The most careful attention must be given to the proper construction and adjustment of the key pads. The pads are made from a strong cloth-like stuff of fine wool [felt]. In order that the pads may close the holes air tight, these felt disks are covered with a fine membrane (skin); this membrane is usually doubled, so that any accidental injury to the pad shall not become troublesome all at once.

The pads are covered over on the back side with little sheets of card and a hole is punched through the center, so that they may be screwed fast in the key cups. It is hardly possible to make the key cups always come exactly to the edge of the tone-holes; the pads are therefore made of such thickness that there is left a little space, then by underlaying of card or paper disks this may be filled till the pad fits perfectly all around. The failure of the pad to close the hole at particular points can be remedied by using pieces of paper cut in crescent shape.

The pads are held by screws, the nuts being soldered to the key cups, and under the heads of the little screws there are silver washers, which must be allowed to press the pad neither too tightly nor too lightly; in the first case little wrinkles are formed in the skin of the pad which interfere with the air tight closing, in the second case air may escape through the cup.

If a washer is too loosely held by its screw, it may be set in vibration by certain tones, producing an audible buzz which is inexplicable to many. It has happened that flutes have been sent from distances of several hundred miles for repairs on which there was nothing wrong except that one single screw was not sufficiently tight.

The main point about the pads is that each separate key must close the corresponding hole perfectly air tight; and when one key is required to operate upon another this can be accurately adjusted by means of the regulating screws applied by me.

When one key acts upon another, as the E key upon the G key, one can determine by seeing light between the pad and its seat or by the pressure of the finger whether one key presses too hard or too lightly; the regulating screw must be turned backward or forward until the two keys close together.

In the case of the double connected keys, where the F♯ key works the G key and the B key together, first turn the adjusting screw in the clutch of the F♯ key, and regulate the action of the G key, and then, afterwards adjust the action of the B key.

To prove that all the keys on the middle joint or on the foot joint close perfectly, stop one end with a fine cork, and blow into the other end, while all the keys are closed with the fingers; one can then determine whether or not the air leaks out. By strongly blowing in tobacco smoke it will be easily seen which key leaks. But, a more certain way is to draw out the air, after which the fingers are removed; if then all the keys remain closed of themselves, it is a sure indication no air leaks in.

Fig. 38 is a clamp made of steel wire with which the keys can be pressed upon the flute until the pads become perfectly seated.

FIG. 38.   Clamp for the pads.

Upon removing a pad which is still useful, one should designate its correct position in relation to the key stem by a mark, so that upon replacing it, it will come exactly into its former position.

I have given these explanations so minutely, because the certain speaking and pure quality of tone of a flute depend in a great measure upon a perfect closing of the key, and this again upon a good padding. Well made pads, which I have in stock, can easily be sent in letters as "samples without value."

(d) THE SPRINGS

Of all metals, steel, undoubtedly, is the best for making springs. The genuine English darning or sewing needles of fine cast steel, well hardened, perfectly polished, which can be had in all

required lengths and thicknesses, the best fulfill
all the requirements of good key springs.

Their preparation is quite simple. When it is
necessary to replace a broken spring by a new
one, select a needle of the proper length and of
exactly the same thickness as the broken one,
accurately fitting the hole in the spring post, so
that it may be drawn in tight without being drawn
through. When a proper needle is found, lay it
on a thin piece of sheet iron, and hold it over
an alcohol flame long enough for it to become uniformly of a beautiful blue or dark violet color.
It thus loses its too great brittleness, and it can be
easily bent as much as is necessary for obtaining
the required tension, without danger of breaking.
The needle may then be notched with a file at the
right length and the superfluous end broken off.
For this a fine sharp edged file is useful. The
bending and inserting of the springs is accomplished by means of small pincers, Fig. 39.

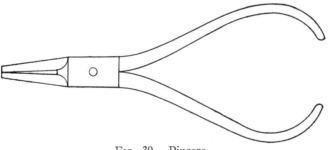

Fig. 39. Pincers.

If steel springs break, it is almost always because of rust, which readily forms in damp air

or from the perspiration of the fingers. A sudden breaking of a spring while playing is very disagreeable. To prevent this, I have sometimes made springs of hard-drawn gold wire, which cost only 4 Thalers extra; these are next to steel springs in elasticity, and for many years have proved themselves very durable.

(e) The Cork in the Head Joint

Since the perfect tuning of the octaves depends upon the proper closing of the air column by the cork, it is necessary to smear it well with tallow each time it is drawn out for wiping the head joint.

If the cork fits too tightly, it can be made a little smaller by rolling between two smooth surfaces such as a table top and small board. Conversely the cork may be made shorter and consequently thicker by means of a cabinet maker's screw clamp.

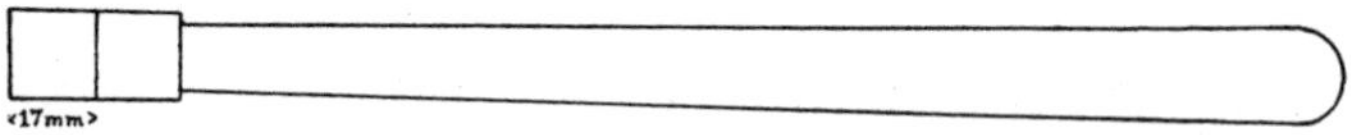

<17mm>

FIG. 40. Gauge for setting the cork.

That one may always place the cork exactly at the correct distance of 17 millimeters [about $\frac{11}{16}$ inch] from the center of the mouth-hole, it is best to have a mark on the projecting end of the cork screw, and for verification to have also an accurate measuring stick such as is shown in Fig. 40.

THEOBALD BOEHM

Aged 33 years

From a miniature painted on ivory by Brandmüller

IX. TREATMENT OF THE FLUTE IN GENERAL

IN order that a flute may remain in good condition as long as possible, it must be handled with care and cleanliness. Generally one has only himself to blame for the larger repairs required, for cracks in the wood or breaks in the mechanism are usually the result of carelessness and neglect of cleanliness. Such accidents are easily prevented. If the cork coverings of both joints of the middle part of a wood flute are well rubbed with pure tallow, they will then remain soft and will tightly close the joints against moisture; and the application of undue force when putting the parts together will become unnecessary. For the same reason, the draw tube of the head joint, and the socket tube on the lower end of the middle joint of a silver flute must always be covered with tallow.

To avoid injury to the key mechanism, the middle joint should always be grasped by the upper end, and never in the middle; and similarly the foot-joint should be grasped with the hand on the lower end.

The three pieces should be so put together that the flute may be held in a natural position. The mouth-hole, the centers of the upper holes on the middle joint, and the axles of the foot keys should coincide in one straight line. The crutch should be inserted and so turned that the weight of the flute rests between the thumb and index finger of the left hand, then the movements of the fingers will be much freer than when the thumb is used for holding the flute. [The crutch is shown at *C* in Figs. 27 and 28, and also in Fig. 33.]

[The translator agrees with Rockstro, who, in his "Treatise on the Flute," says: "The crutch is a cumbersome and unsightly appendage, and is useless to those who have properly constructed flutes, and who know how to hold them. It seriously cramps the action of the left hand fingers, especially the thumb, while it is unproductive of a single advantage. Happily it is now almost obsolete."]

Further, one should be certain that the flute is so held in the hand that no water can flow into the tone-holes, since pads covered with moisture easily stick to the edges of the holes.

When the flute is laid down out of the hand, the crutch should be turned at right angles to the flute tube so that it will form a firm support for the flute as it rests upon a horizontal plane, the flute tube itself inclining downwards.

If a pad should become accidentally wet and for this reason or because of dirt, should stick, push a strip of printing paper under the pad and again draw it out while gently pressing down on the key. In this way the moisture and dirt will be rubbed off the smooth skin of the pad, and will adhere to the rough surface of the paper.

If one takes the further slight trouble, each

time the flute is laid down, to wipe the perspiration of the fingers from the keys, the oxidation of the metal will be retarded, and the flute will remain clean and bright for a long time.

The most important matter in the care of flutes, especially of new wooden ones, is the wiping out of the tube. The warping out of shape of the wood, which alters the proportions of the bore, and causes most of the cracks, is the result of moisture, which collects in the flute tube during the blowing. This produces an unequal expansion, the consequence of which is often the formation of superficial ridges, and frequently the complete bursting of the wood.

Consequently after each blowing the flute tube must be wiped perfectly clean and dry, for which purpose one had best use an old silk or fine linen handkerchief and a thin swab stick of the length of the middle joint. Fold one end of the corner of the cloth over the stick and push it through the flute, till the upper end can be taken hold of. Then by slowly drawing the cloth through, all the drops of the liquid will be taken up by the first part of the cloth while the following part which is yet dry will completely remove any remaining moisture.

Upon repeating this operation many times the bore will become polished, facilitating the full and easy production of tone; and this also makes it entirely superfluous to oil the flute tube, which is both disagreeable and injurious to the pads.

X. ON THE BLOWING OF NEW FLUTES

EXPERIENCE shows that all wood-wind instruments are affected by the manner of blowing so that they become either better or worse with regard to the tones and their production. Though the tuning proportions remain unaltered, yet the player can accustom himself to blow single tones higher or lower.

The reasons for this have never yet been satisfactorily explained. But it is known, that even after all swellings and deformations of the wood are removed from the flute tube as much as possible by the most careful swabbings, the influence of the manner of blowing still remains perceptible. The best flute loses an easy speech by overblowing and its bright clear quality of tone by a bad embouchure, and conversely gains in speech and tone by a correct handling and a good embouchure.

The formation of a good embouchure is therefore not only of the utmost importance for flute playing in general, but especially for the blowing of new flutes. Consequently a knowledge of the origin of the tone will be helpful.

THEOBALD BOEHM

Aged 35 years

At the time of the development of the conical bore, ring-key, flute

XI. THE EMBOUCHURE

THE column of air enclosed by the tube of the flute is exactly comparable with a stretched violin string. As the string is set into transverse vibrations by the bow and thus is made to sound, so the longitudinal vibrations of the air column of the flute are produced by the blowing.

Further, as the clear quality of tone of the violin depends upon a proper manipulation of the bow, so also the pure flute tone depends upon the direction in which the air stream is blown against the edge of the mouth-hole.

Depending upon whether the air stream is directed more or less below the horizontal as it is blown across the flute, there develops from the fundamental tone of the flute tube, with all the holes closed, the so-called aliquot or harmonic overtones; e. g., for the fundamental tone C_3, the aliquot tones are C_4, G_4, C_5, E_5, G_5, $(B_5\flat)$, and C_6.

Each octave therefore requires a different direction of the air stream, and when the correct one is found, not merely will a fine quality of tone be brought out, but by increasing the force of the air blast, the tone may be brought to the greatest possible strength without any deterioration in quality or pitch.

However, by overblowing, that is by violently

forcing the air, any tone can be made to break over into the higher tones, even when only a portion of the air goes in the right direction. Not only through the air thus wasted, but also because of the poor embouchure, the tone loses in purity, and there is produced at the same time a buzzing and rushing noise.

XII. THE BASS FLUTE IN G

(a) Its Musical Characteristics

IN closing [in the original this section appeared at the end of the "Conclusion"] I feel that I ought to mention one of the most recently perfected, and therefore little known, developments of the flute, to the construction of which I was led by the great facility of vibration and easy speech of my silver flute in C; I refer to the "Alt-Flöte" in G [Bass Flute] which is pitched a major fourth below the flute in C.

The long felt need for deeper, stronger, and at the same time more sonorous flute tones has not been satisfactorily provided for either by the former "Flûte d'amour" or by the extension to the foot of a C flute, since the tones thus obtained are weak and uncertain, and their combination difficult and entirely unpracticable. There must be created an entirely new instrument in the family of flutes of deeper pitch, similar to the bassethorn and the English horn.

[The exact date of the origin of the bass flute is uncertain. The booklet, "Zur Erinnerung an Theobald Boehm," states: "In his sixtieth year Boehm made his Alt-Flöte which produces a remarkable effect." This would make the year **1854** or **1855**. In several letters dated in 1865, Boehm refers to the flute in G as being well established.]

[Fig. 41 shows a bass flute in G made by Boehm and Mendler, acording to their most approved design. Fig. 42 is an instrument of the same kind with slight improvements in the mechanism, made by Rudall, Carte and Company.]

Because of the great facility for modulation of the full, sonorous tones of this flute, it is adapted to music in the song style, and for accompanying a soprano voice. A player will, after a very little practice, be in a position to bring out *genre* effects which are impossible upon the C flute.

[Flutists have sometimes misunderstood the purpose of the flute in G, thinking it ought to be like the flute in C in quality but lower in pitch. It was Boehm's purpose to produce "an entirely new instrument," with a quality distinctly different from that of the flute in C even when tones of the same pitch were sounded on both flutes. The difference is similar to that between a true soprano voice and a true contralto. The quality of the lower register of the flute in G sometimes mildly suggests tones of the same pitch of the violin, or the French horn, or the saxophone played softly.]

[Flutes of low pitch have long been made by many makers, often descending a full octave below middle C, as in the so-called contra-bass flutes. An account of flutes of lower pitch is given in Chapter VIII of Fitzgibbon's "Story of the Flute," reprinted in the *Flutist* magazine for November, 1920, page 244. Boehm's distinct contribution was in so proportioning the tube as to secure the

FIG. 41.
Bass Flute
Boehm & Mendler

FIG. 42.
Bass Flute
Rudall, Carte & Co.

desired characteristic tone-quality, and in so arranging the key mechanism that the fingering remains the same as for the Flute in C, and so that the operation is as certain and easy. The flute in G plays very easily, with an embouchure a little more relaxed than for the flute in C, and with gentler blowing; the mechanism is so reliable that the execution is just as clear and certain as for the flute in C, though on account of the larger size of the keys, it is not suitable for very rapid passages. Its effective compass is about two and a half octaves. A Flute in F becomes so long that the mechanism is less satisfactory in operation. On the other hand the Alto Flute in Bb is as playable as the flute in C, and is intermediate between this and the flute in G as regards tone quality.]

[In a letter to Mr. Broadwood dated August, 1871, (Broadwood, "Essay," page 59), Boehm writes: "My ideal of tone, large, sonorous, and powerful, admitting of every gradation from *pianissimo* to *fortissimo*, is still the tone of my silver flute in G. The effect I have repeatedly produced, when playing it, although now I am an old man of 78½ years, is such that I only regret that I did not make this flute forty years ago. With a silver head-joint and a gold embouchure, the tone is very brilliant, and no room is too large for it; while with a wood embouchure on the silver head-joint, the tone gains in richness without losing in power. Once when I played in church on this flute, accompanying a soprano, it was mis-

taken for a French horn." In another letter dated
February, 1873, he writes: "My eightieth birth-
day will be in a few weeks, nevertheless I play
every morning on my flute in G and people like to
hear it." The translator has used a flute in G for
over twenty years, and very much prefers it to the
flute in C for music in the song style.]

[Notwithstanding its beautiful tone quality the
flute in G has been used but little. However,
modern orchestral composers are now scoring for
it, parts being found in the following compositions: Ravel, *Daphnis et Chloe;* Weingarten, *Die
Gefilde der Seligen;* Mahler, *Symphonies;* Hol-
brooke, *Children of Don* and *Dylan;* Stanford, various compositions; Hahn, *A Ballet;* Schmid, *Joseph
and His Brethren;* Stravinsky, *Le Sacre du Prin-
temps;* Rimsky-Karsakow, *Ballet Mlada,* and *Ivan
the Terrible;* Glazunow, various compositions;
Atterberg, *Ocean Symphony.*]

[The flute in G is particularly suited to chamber music, solos, duets, trios, etc., and yet very
little music has ever been published for it. Rudall,
Carte and Company, of London, have issued the
following pieces for the flute in G and piano:
Beethoven, *Adelaide;* Mendelssohn, *Elijah, If With
All Your Hearts* and *O, Rest in the Lord;* Mozart,
Aria, *Il mio tesoro,* and *Andante* (arranged by
Boehm); Schubert, *Serenade.* Boehm arranged
a number of pieces but these have remained in
manuscript with the single exception noted above;
a list of these arrangements is given in the appendix, and probably any flutist can himself re-

arrange them from other available scores. Violin
music of the song style is especially suitable, as
the flute in G begins on the same tone as the G
string of the violin. The part for the violin may
be easily transposed. The following pieces have
been found very effective: Bach, *Air for the G
String* (Wilhelmj); Godard, *Adagio Pathétique;*
Schumann, *Träumerei* and *Abendgebet;* Godard,
Berceuse from Jocelyn; Terschak, *Romance Itali-
enne.* Many trios for Flute, Violin, and Piano are
beautifully rendered when the Flute in G takes
the violin part; an effective number of this kind is
the *Romanza* by Fuchs.]

(b)   Dimensions of the Bass Flute

As early as 1847 I had made flute tubes giving
an easy and certain speech for the tone E_2

but the difficulties connected with the construction
and playing of the keys led me to choose the
tone G_2

as the fundamental of my bass flute.

In the calculation of the proportions of the air
column, I gave preference to the deeper tones;
the speech is easy and certain, and lends itself to
a surprisingly strong *crescendo;* hence the bass
flute is suitable for playing in the largest room or
in the *salon.*

[Boehm submitted a flute in G, together with an explanation of his *Schema*, to the Paris Exposition of 1867, and as a part of the exhibit there were tables of the actual dimensions of his flutes in C and G. The table for the flute in C is given on page 35 of this work; the table for the Flute in G was not included by Boehm in "Die Flöte und das Flötenspiel," but for the sake of completeness and because of increasing interest, it seems desirable to include it in this edition. Comments on the exhibit at the Paris Exhibition are given on pages 309 to 313 of Welch's "History of the Boehm Flute."]

[As made by Boehm the flute in G has a tube with an inside diameter of 26 millimeters; the tone-holes are 19.3 millimeters in diameter and the rise of the keys is about 6 millimeters; the embouchure is a trifle larger than for the flute in C, being about 11.0 by 13.0 millimeters; the distance of the face of the cork from the center of the embouchure is 20.5 millimeters; Table III gives the scale for such a flute corresponding to the pitch A=435. From these dimensions a *Schema* diagram for the flute in G at various pitches can be constructed in the manner described for the flute in C, on pages 35 to 47. The "actual length of air column" for any tone is the distance, measured from the face of the cork to the center of the corresponding lateral tone-hole having a diameter of 19.3 millimeters. This length is 68 millimeters less than the corresponding "theoretical length"; the quantity, 68 millimeters, is the "closed-end correction" for this size of tube (see pages 34 and 42).]

TABLE III

Tones	Absolute Vibration Numbers	Theoretical Lengths of Air Column	Actual Lengths of Air Column
G_3	387.54	442.50mm	374.50mm
$G_3\flat$ $F_3\sharp$	365.79	468.81	400.81
F_3	345.26	496.68	428.68
E_3	325.88	526.22	458.22
$E_3\flat$ $D_3\sharp$	307.59	557.51	489.51
D_3	290.33	590.66	522.66
$D_3\flat$ $C_3\sharp$	274.03	625.78	557.78
C_3	258.65	663.00	595.00
B_2	244.14	702.42	634.42
$B_2\flat$ $A_2\sharp$	230.43	733.19	676.19
A_2	217.50	788.44	720.44
$A_2\flat$ $G_2\sharp$	205.29	835.32	767.32
G_2	193.77	885.00	817.00

[Other practical details of the dimensions, for the pitch A=435, are as follows: The "correction for the open end" is 10.5 millimeters, so that the distance from the cork, to the end giving the lowest tone, G_2, is 817+10.5=827.5 millimeters. The correction for the F♯ hole is – 2.3 millimeters, giving for the actual location of this hole, 557.8 – 2.3= 555.5 millimeters from the cork. The C♯ hole is 10 millimeters in diameter and it is at a distance of 333.0 millimeters from the cork. The D♮ trill-key hole has a diameter of 10.5 millimeters and it is 315.2 millimeters from the cork. The octave-key hole is 5.0 millimeters in diameter and is 13.9 millimeters above the C♯ hole.]

[The bass flute shown in Fig. 41 is constructed according to the *Schema* based upon the dimensions of Table III, and is for the pitch A=440.]

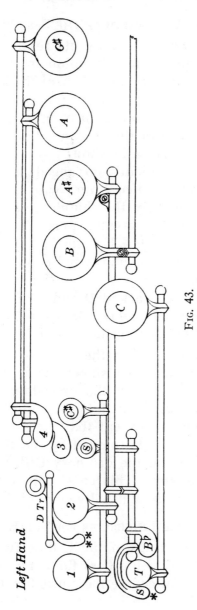

Fig. 43.

Upper part of the key mechanism of the Bass Flute.

(c) MECHANISM OF THE BASS FLUTE

Being made with G for its fundamental tone, there is required no alteration in the system of fingering, since the upper half of the key mechanism can be arranged to be played very conveniently by the left hand, through extensions of the axles, as shown in Fig. 43, and the lower half requires only slight alterations.

A very conveniently arranged "schleifklappe" [octave-key], marked S and with a * in Fig. 43, may be opened by the thumb; it serves to give freer speech and greater purity of tone to the notes $D_4\sharp$, $E_4\flat$, D_5, $D_5\sharp$, $E_5\flat$ and A_5. [This key is described and illustrated, as applied to the flute in C, on page 86.]

The trill key, marked D and * * in Fig. 43, is a substitute for the long D trill key in all cases where this would be used on the C flute.

[The mechanism of the flute shown in Fig. 41 is arranged exactly as shown in the diagram Fig. 43, and explained in the preceding paragraphs. The mechanism of the flute shown in Fig. 42 is the same in general, except that there are trill keys for D and D♯, to be played by the fingers of the right hand as on the ordinary C flute, and there is no octave-key. This construction for the trill keys is the one now usually employed.]

(d) SPECIAL FINGERINGS FOR THE BASS FLUTE

All the fingerings of the C flute from C_3 to A_5 are applicable to the bass flute; but since the C_3 sounds as G_2, of course the music for the bass flute

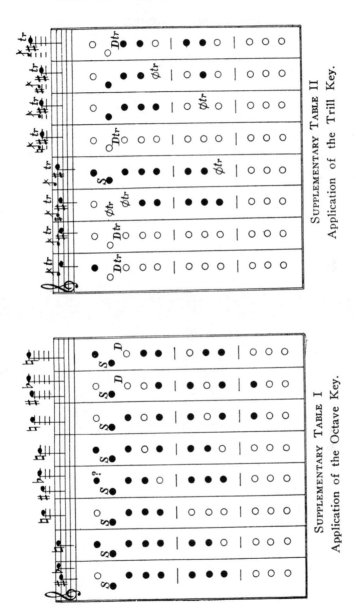

SUPPLEMENTARY TABLE II
Application of the Trill Key.

SUPPLEMENTARY TABLE I
Application of the Octave Key.

must be written a fourth higher, that is, be transposed. [The tables of regular fingerings for the C flute are given on page 72.]

On p. 129 are two supplementary tables of fingerings; the first shows the application of the octave-key *, Fig. 43; the second table indicates the special uses of the D trill key, * *, Fig. 43. [As mentioned above, the bass flute is usually constructed with trill keys placed as on the C flute, in which case the fingerings for the latter are directly applicable.]

THEOBALD BOEHM

Aged 60 years

At the time of the perfection of the cylinder bore, covered hole, flute

His favorite portrait

PART II

—

FLUTE-PLAYING

PART II—FLUTE-PLAYING

XIII. THE DEVELOPMENT OF TONE

UPON the supposition that the student has had elementary musical instruction in regard to notes, time, keys, etc., such as may be found in any printed Flute Instructor (especially in that of Hugot and Wunderlich, Jos. Aibl, Munich) I will proceed to a consideration of the playing of the flute itself, and shall begin with what I believe to be the essential requisite, the tone formation.

A good embouchure depends for the most part upon a normal formation of the lips and teeth. However, if one has a defective embouchure, and also lacks a proper appreciation of beautiful tone quality, that is if he does not have a proper tone sense, both of these faults can be considerably improved by exercising in the following manner.

Since a gradual transition is best in all things, by passing from the easy to the more difficult, so one, in blowing a new flute, should not begin with the higher and lower tones which are more difficult to produce, but he should begin in the middle register, in which the tone C_4 is best produced by a beginner. [This tone is produced when the first finger of the left hand only is placed on its key.]

When one has found the proper embouchure by which this tone can be clearly sounded in a delicate *piano,* one should gradually, without raising the pitch, swell it to a *forte,* and then bring it back again to the faintest *pianissimo.*

When this is fully accomplished one passes in the following manner to the next lower tone. While sounding the C₄ with a beautiful, clear, and pure tone, close the C key by a quick motion [of the left thumb], but without making any alteration in the embouchure or in the force of the wind.

The tone B thus obtained should continue, un-altered, the quality and purity of the preceding tone C. Then sound the B alone [with *crescendo*

and *diminuendo*], and after breathing again, pro-ceed [in like manner] to the tone B♭.

Continuing in this way and with the least pos-sible alteration of the embouchure, gradually, cer-tainly and without exertion proceed to the lower tones successively, and in a similar manner prac-tice the tones from C₄ upwards to the highest. Since each tone is always developed out of the preceding tone, which is already as perfect as possible, all of the tones will remain equally perfect in quality, strength and purity.

As soon as one obtains a certainty in the embouchure, he should next practice all the major and minor scales; then intervals of thirds, fourths, fifths, sixths, sevenths, and octaves; the embouchure will thus become accustomed to the making of increasing intervals, and soon one will be in a position to take the greatest skips with the proper embouchure, and consequently with certainty.

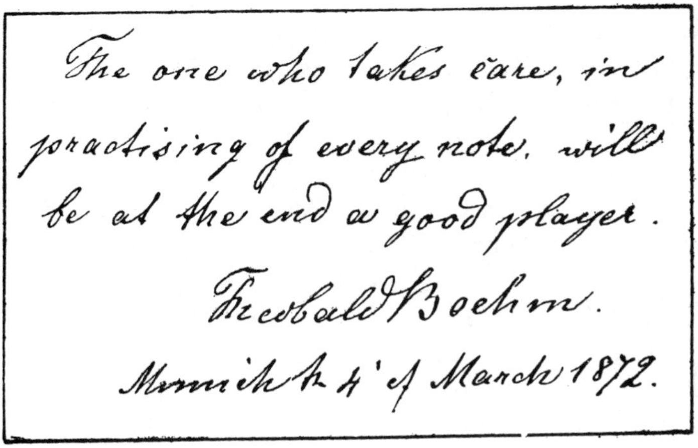
The one who takes care, in
practising of every note, will
be at the end a good player.
Theobald Boehm.
Munich the 4' of March 1872.

FIG. 44.
Facsimile of Boehm's autograph.

XIV. FINGER EXERCISES

SINCE the certain production of the tone depends not only upon the embouchure, but also upon a quick and smooth movement of the fingers, in this exercise all the tones should be slurred together, for in staccato playing one observes less easily whether all the fingers move up and down precisely together.

A portion of one's attention is always lost in reading notes, therefore, it is very important to play "by heart" as much as possible, so that the formation of the embouchure and tone may have the undivided attention. To do this will, of course, be difficult for the untrained musician. The best method for impressing upon the memory the proper sequence of tones in the scales and chords of all keys, is first to learn by heart the tones of one scale or one chord in only a single octave; then one will soon learn to play the flute in all keys and through its entire compass. Furthermore I have come to the conclusion from my own practice as well as from my many years of experience as a teacher, that pupils advance most rapidly who take the trouble to practice patiently the complicated finger changes of a single difficult phrase until it can be played smoothly and clearly. One acquires in this way, so to speak, wealth which is laid by, and which is always increasing by additions.

When a short phrase is found difficult, it is evidently a waste of time to repeat the entire passage containing the "stumbling block" in the greater part of which one has already acquired facility; one should practice the few troublesome notes till the difficult tone-combination is mastered.

By such a judicious use of time I have brought many scholars in a year's practice to a thoroughly correct interpretation (execution) of a piece of music which others with far greater talent, but without patience and perseverance, would never acquire.

An answer is needed to the question which is so frequently put to me, "What and how should one first practice in learning my flute?" Notwithstanding this work makes no claim to the title of a Flute-School, yet this is an appropriate place for the answer and the many interested flute players will welcome it.

XV. THE METHOD OF PRACTICING

ABOVE all one should endeavor, at the beginning of each practice period, to secure a good embouchure, in the manner previously described, for without a clear tone, nothing can be well and beautifully played. The tone is the voice without which one cannot even begin to sing.

When the embouchure has become good and certain, one should study the scales and chords in all the keys, for these are the foundation of all passages, and when one has once learned to play them with precise finger movements (which can be easily determined by the ear) all the other tone figures will be quickly and easily mastered.

As has been said, it is only a waste of time to repeat anything that can already be played without stumbling. Difficult finger movements, on the contrary, must be gone over very slowly at first, so that in the slurred tone-combinations no interpolated tones are audible, and no lack of purity is noticeable. Especially, one must train the fingers to a perfectly smooth movement by the trill exercises, so that no one tone predominates, and so that no bleating or so-called "bockstriller" [goat trill] is produced.

To secure this smoothness, there must be no perceptible cramping tension of the muscles, in either the hand or arm; this cramping results from an entirely unnecessary expenditure of force.

If one only forms the idea that a thing is not difficult, it becomes much easier.

Further, many flute players have the bad habit of raising the fingers not only much too high, but also to unequal heights, whereby complicated finger movements become unnecessarily difficult; since when several keys are closed at the same time, if one finger must move much farther than another, it is perfectly evident that they cannot reach the end at the same time.

The raising of the fingers too high has another disadvantage, since in rapidly closing the keys a very audible and disagreeable clap or rattle is produced, and at the same time the key receives a blow and the mechanism a reaction which clearly work disadvantageously to them. On the contrary, if the fingers are held directly over the keys a forcible closing of them will be nearly or wholly inaudible, and there will be produced only a pressure without rebound.

The fingers therefore should be held at equal heights, and no higher than is necessary above the keys. To secure this, and especially as most players do not realize how high they have raised their fingers, I advise all my pupils, when practicing the scales, to stand before a mirror. They are then in a position to see not only the finger movements and the whole manner of holding the flute, but also to detect many bad habits, such as distortion of the features, and unnecessary movements of the head, arms and body.

If one cannot express his feelings through the style of tone, he surely is not in a position to do so by head or body movements. A calm, firm attitude certainly presents a much more pleasing appearance to the hearer than visible exertions, or affected, sentimental movements.

Since bad habits are very difficult to overcome, they ought to be removed in their beginnings. It is very short sighted to economize in the beginning, for in the end the best teacher is also the cheapest. It is impossible for everyone to find a good teacher, and in all the flute-schools known to me the methods of style are treated in a very superficial manner; therefore, I believe that my views upon this subject, founded upon many years of experience as an artist and teacher, should be given.

ANTOINE SACCHETTI AND THEOBALD BOEHM

XVI. MUSICAL INTERPRETATION

HE who, like myself, has been fortunate enough to have heard, for more than fifty years, all the greatest singers and songstresses of the time, will never forget the names of Brizzi, Sesi, Catalani, Velluti, Lablache, Tamburini, Rubini, Malibran, Pasta, etc. It fills me with joy to remember their artistic and splendid performances; they have all come forth from the good old Italian school of song, which today, as in the past hundred years, gives the foundation for a good voice formation, and leads to a correct understanding of style, which is an essential for the instrumentalist as well as for the singer.

The interpretation of a piece of music should evidently give to the hearer what the composer has endeavored to express in notes. The player himself must therefore, in order to be intelligible, first clearly comprehend the sense and spirit of the composition.

But the means which the composer has at hand are not always sufficient to clearly convey his ideas. All the customary designations of the tempo from *largo* to *prestissimo* being without metronomic determinations give rather indefinite ideas; and the articulations, accents, and nuances of the tone strength, especially in older or carelessly copied music, are designated at the best in a very faulty way and often not at all. Much is left therefore to the discretion and individual comprehension of the performer, in which respects, as is known, even thorough musicians will differ considerably.

In the orchestra, naturally the interpretation of the director is followed and the flutist who plays each note according to the dictated directions, clearly, with a good and pure tone, has accomplished much, and his playing is at least correct.

In solo playing, on the other hand, where the player himself appears, the overcoming of technical difficulties is mainly accomplished by an extraordinary amount of practice, after which the genuine artist should endeavor to bring out a definite expression of feeling. It is much easier to win applause by a brilliant execution, than to reach the hearts of the hearers through a *cantabile*.

For example, to play well an *adagio* with all the possible colorature, the player must not only be a perfect master of his instrument, but he must also have the power to transform the tones, as it were, into words, by which he will be able to give his feelings a clear expression. The composer of vocal music endeavors to make the tones express the emotions described by the words, and the singer is most easily led to a correct musical interpretation through the words connected with the tones; likewise, the flute player must learn to sing upon his instrument.

If the composer under the influence of the words

of the poem has been enabled to express his feelings in tone, and to form his melodies upon the laws of rhythm and declamation, so also the thoughtful instrumentalist can perceive the correct interpretation of the music of an aria or a song in its text.

He will learn by the study of good song music when and why a note should be played staccato, or be slurred with the next following; and when an accent or a crescendo or diminuendo in the tone strength, is necessary to bestow upon the music an expression corresponding to the words; and when a breath can be taken without breaking the correct declamation.

The text will clearly show him the phrases and will indicate to him the points for which the full strength of the tone must be saved, for producing the greatest effects, as is done by the points of highest light in a good painting.

The following examples will serve as a clearer explanation of what has been said, as well as to explain the *portamento di voce* which is indispensable to a good style of cantabile.

Since it is only possible to indicate the declamation or correct expression of the words of a text on an instrument by means of articulation, that is by striking the notes according to the meaning or syllable-beginnings of the words, it is important to learn the necesary art of tonguing and its proper application. This is indicated in three different ways, namely a short staccato by little lines

(𝄽𝄽𝄽)   ; less staccato by points   (𝄽𝄽𝄽)

and an entirely smooth staccato by points over

which there is a slur   (𝄽𝄽𝄽) , indicating that

the tone is to have merely a new impulse, but that
the air stream is not to be interrupted.

This tonguing should sound as softly as the
second syllable "de" [tē] for example, in speaking
the word "Beide" [bī-tē], which serves very satisfactorily for the making of separate syllables. In
many cases the expression can be further increased, as is indicated in the following example.

[The musical illustrations have been photographically reproduced from the German edition.
The line above the words is the music as written
for the voice, while the line below indicates the
interpretation for the flute.]

The correct articulation follows here of itself
from the declamation of the words.

By means of the soft tonguing of the four notes Eb, D, C, and Bb of the first bar, as well as the notes D, C, Bb and Ab of the third bar, there is given to the words "ist bezaubernd schön," and "kein Auge je gesehn," considerably more expression than if they were entirely slurred together. The breathing places are indicated thus: v.

Further, it is evident that it is not allowable to slur any note over to the first note of the next measure, since it almost always happens that the note falling in the so-called strong part of the measure must be tongued, in order that the word depending upon it may receive its proper accent. The slurring of a note to the following measure is always a fault, unless it is justified for some special reason, as in dance music or comic songs, where it may be used to produce a piquant or bizarre effect. For example:

But in song music this tying over from the weak to the strong beat of a measure is allowable only when employed as syncopation, as in canon or fugue, to bring out an increased expression. For example in the following illustration where the

word "nur" is repeated in the third measure, the anticipation of the E by a quarter note constitutes a syncopation, by means of which the effect is increased.

The following examples will furnish, through a reading of the text, a clear idea of the rhythmic and declamatory significance of each note.

The methods of interpretation which I have here given for playing on the flute, will serve as guides by which anyone may learn to judge correctly why and in what manner a note should be tongued or intoned, so that it shall give the sense and expression of the word for which it is a substitute, or whether it should be considered merely as a syllable without significance, and should therefore be slurred together with other notes.

Upon the repetition of a strophe, on the contrary, where the theme would become somewhat monotonous in the absence of words, the player may be allowed to take some license, and add little ornaments in suitable places; especially in bright and light melodies. In the last of the following songs, "Das Fischermädchen," for example, a heightening of the expression will result, if the ornaments are performed not heavily, but lightly and gracefully.

In the preceding song the triplets, and also the sixteenth notes of the second, fourth and sixth measures of the following, may be slurred; however, in my opinion, a soft tonguing gives a more definite effect.

Ständchen.

The triplets may also be slurred together, in the above song.

Das Fischermädchen.

The great wealth of beautiful German songs of Mozart, Beethoven, Schubert, Mendelssohn and others are almost inexhaustible sources of studies for the formation of a correct interpretation and a good style.

From the words of the poems of the popular songs of other nations, such as Scottish, Irish, Swedish and Slavish, one may also learn a good interpretation.

One should begin with songs which are simple but full of expression in word and melody, then one will soon learn to comprehend compositions, which, as Beethoven's "Adelaide," are written in the highest dramatic style, and form a transition to the arias for the interpretation of which a knowledge of all the arts of ornamentation and colorature is necessary.

All coloratures may be considered a diversification of a single note, whose time value is partially or wholly consumed in executing the ornaments.

The simplest ornament is the accented appoggiatura which moves either upwards or downwards, and is designated by a small note; and for equally divided notes it takes one-half of the time value of the principal note, and for unequal division it takes one-third.

Schreibweise.   Ausführung.

[The musical ornaments are first given "as written," and then "as played;" in some instances the name or interpretation seems to be incorrect.]

The double appoggiatura, consisting of two or three small notes, is to be treated in a similar manner. This may form a triplet, as in the examples:

The double appoggiatura is to be distinguished from the "schneller" or half-mordent in which the first of the two small notes is always the same as the principal note; for example:

The true mordent (gruppetto) is a group of three or four small notes which move within the compass of a minor third, and consists, both in ascending and descending, of a note first above and then below the given note. For example:

A very effective, and at the same time the most difficult vocal ornament is the trill, a thoroughly good execution of which is, at the present time, unfortunately, very rarely heard. The trill consists in the alternation of two adjacent tones, a major or a minor second part, which are to be smoothly and rapidly repeated. Following the best old Italian school of song, the trill should commence upon the principal note, and not upon the auxiliary note; the two notes must have equal tone strength, and exactly equal time value, and

the alternation should be slower in Adagio, and
more rapid in Allegro. For a final cadence, or a
fermata, it should gradually increase in speed, and
there should be a swelling out and a diminishing
of the tone strength. Further, every trill must
end with a resolution which is formed of the principal note preceded by the next lower note. The
"Pralltriller" [inverted mordent] is the only exception to this rule. For a cadence trill the end-
ing may have a variety of forms, according to the
taste of the performer.

Cadence trill.

Prall trill.

According to my idea, all trills not resting upon
the note of the harmony, such as the last preceding

mordent trills, and trills consisting in the multi-
plication of an appoggiatura, should begin with

the auxiliary note, and proceed by means of a final resolution.

All trills must begin slowly, and very gradually become more rapid, a perfect equality of the tones being maintained throughout, and the production of a so-called bleating or "bockstriller" must be avoided.

Equally useful are the ornaments produced by runs, which are also developed by the diversification of a fundamental tone and which must therefore be played exactly within the time and in the manner of expression of this note; either with equal tone value (*tenuto*) or with increasing strength (*crescendo*) or diminishing strength (*diminuendo*). For example:

Since the time of Mozart, and especially by Rossini, all the vocal ornaments have been accurately written out by composers, hence one will find in operas and concert arias a large selection of tasteful and effective coloratures, which will serve as models for practice.

Many arias also contain the most beautiful melodies for the study of cantabile which in æsthetic respects will remain the best examples, and for the rendering of which the flute player must have all the qualifications which characterize the genuine artist. These qualifications are an intelligent comprehension of the composition, a deep feeling and a cultivated taste, correctly timed breathing, and a perfectly formed tone, for without these a good interpretation of a cantabile with *portamento* (gliding voice) is impossible.

Although the proper *portamento di voce,* namely the gliding over from one tone to another while speaking two different syllables, is adapted to the human voice alone, and consequently seldom seems good and appropriate on string instruments, yet it is sometimes desired to imitate it upon wind instruments with tone holes. On account of defective execution, however, the effect is often repulsive and suggests "cat music" on the house tops, rather than a beautifully sung *cantilena.*

The significance, often misunderstood, of the word *portamento,* seems to me to consist in a development of the legato derived from the Italian *cantare legato* in which all the intermediate tones are delicately and smoothly connected together, like a series of pearls by a connecting thread, the latter being figuratively represented by the air stream. For example:

The following extract from the aria of Donna Anna in Mozart's "Don Juan" serves as a combination of the above described song-studies, since the cantibile of the Larghetto ends with simple runs and mordent ornaments, and the Allegretto contains mordent trills, roulades, and a closing trill, and has practically all of the arts of colorature.

In the lower line, designed to be played upon the flute, all of the legato places are designated by slur marks, the moderate articulations by points and the sharply tongued notes by lines. The places where breath should be taken are designated by large breathing signs, and the places where it may be taken if necessary by small signs. [In the original edition there are no staccatissimo lines, and the breathing signs are all alike.] The explanation of the trills which occur has already been given above.

sen - ti - rà sen - ti - rà pie - tà di me, forse un gior - no il cie - lo an -

co - ra sen - ti - ra

pie - tà di me, sen - ti

rà pie - tà pie - tà di me sen - ti rà pie - tà di

me for - se for - se il cie - lo un gior - no sen - ti - rà - pie tà di me

Fig. 45.

A photographic reproduction of No. 1 of the 12 Uebungen, in Boehm's own hand-writing.

XVII.   CONCLUSION

I BELIEVE that I have now pointed out the surest way in which one may acquire a correct and elegant style of playing, so that he may be prepared to delight himself and others not only with difficult compositions, but also with simple and beautifully played songs.

Moreover, attention to my instructions will lead to a correct technical execution, and to facilitate this there has been printed as a supplement to this work and published by Jos. Aibl in Munich, "12 Uebungsstücke in allen Tonarten." These practice pieces form a transition to the following studies which were composed earlier and in which are to be found nearly all the practicable difficulties for the flute.

1. 12 Etudes pour la Flûte, propres a égaliser le doigté dans toutes les gammes, op. 15; Falter & Sohn, Munich; [Rudall, Carte & Co., London; Carl Fischer, New York.]

2. 24 Caprices-Etudes pour la Flûte, op. 26; B. Schott's Söhne, Mainz; Richault, Paris; Rudall, Carte & Co., London; [Carl Fischer, New York.]

3. 24 Etudes pour la Flûte seule ou avec accompagnement du Piano, op. 37; B. Schott's Söhne, Mainz; [Rudall, Carte & Co., London; Carl Fischer, New York.]

[The original manuscript of this work, mentioned in the Preface, contains the first six of the *Uebungsstücke*. No. 1 of the series is photographically reproduced in Fig. 45, and shows the neatness of Boehm's musical hand-writing. These studies are published by the G. Schirmer Company, New York, in the "Library of Musical Classics," Vol. 122, under the title: "Twelve Practice Pieces for Flute for acquiring a smooth and even finger-movement in all keys."]

[Boehm was not only a famous teacher and a member of the Bavarian Royal Court Orchestra, but he was also widely known for his solo playing in concerts. He frequently appeared in many of the principal music centers of Germany, Hungary, Austria, Italy, Switzerland, France, and England, and the printed accounts of his performances are most complimentary. They show that Boehm himself achieved in a remarkable degree the style of playing which he advocates in this treatise. A published account of one of his concerts in Nuremberg contains the following appreciation: "His playing shows a tender, elegiac sentiment, a beautiful, romantic longing; his singing upon his instrument is inspired by the deepest feeling. His mastership in seizing all *nuances,* the melancholy pathos of his style, wins him the first place among the flutists of Europe. One hesitates to breathe for fear the tenderness and soulfulness of the blended tones will be disturbed and the magic spell will be broken." Of a concert given in Leipzig it is written: "The playing of Herr Boehm is firm,

especially pure and technically efficient, with a
beautiful, tender, and yet very full tone. The very
difficult task in Drouet's 'Variations' he gave with
so much finish and good taste that we owe the
artist our thanks for an evening full of enjoyment."]

[Boehm wrote over sixty compositions for the
flute, including original pieces in various styles
and arrangements of the classics, with both piano
and orchestral accompaniments. A complete,
revised list of Boehm's published compositions is
given in the Appendix (c). One of his best compositions is also his last, the Elégie, opus 47,
published in 1881. Schafhäutl, in his "Life of
Boehm," speaks thus of it: "His swan-song bears
the very characteristic title of 'Elégie.' It is
written in the key of A♭ major; a sweet melancholy
rises through forty bars to a bitter lamentation,
only to sink back by degrees to a peaceful resigna-
tion. It is the aged man, who, already ailing, once
said in his eighty-seventh year: 'I would that I
might yet live to the ninetieth year; but as God
wills.' The Elégie is composed for full orchestra.
The orchestra raises the composition to a work
of true magnificence, developing here and there, in
a most effective way, what the singing flute-voice
only suggests."]

Fig. 46.
The house at 20 Altheimereck, Munich, where Boehm lived

Fig. 47.
Inner court, looking toward Boehm's home and shop

APPENDIX

(a) Biographical Notes

Theobald Boehm was born in Munich, Bavaria, on April 9, 1794. He was born, lived, worked, and died in the same house, at No. 20 *Altheimereck*. The Boehm family occupied a flat in a building which had once formed part of one of the religious houses in which before the suppression of such institutions in Bavaria, Munich abounded. It had been the residence of Boehm's father, and his descendants continued to live there. Fig. 46 shows this house, as seen from the street, from a photograph taken by the translator in 1905. The entrance (in the center, at the left of the lamp post) leads into the inner court, and from this court there are various doors and stairways leading to numerous apartments which constitute the building as a whole. Fig. 47 is a view taken in this inner court, looking toward Boehm's apartment. The family lived on the third floor, and the workshops of "Th. Boehm & Mendler" were on the fourth floor just over the living rooms. He was married in 1820. In 1870 there was a celebration of the Golden Wedding, with a family consisting of seven sons, one daughter, seven daughters-in-law, and thirty grandchildren. Boehm died on November 25, 1881, in his eighty-eighth year. In this house on April 9, 1894, there was held a family celebration to commemorate the centenary of Boehm's birth.

Professor Dr. Carl von Schafhäutl, of the University of Munich, was a life-long friend and companion of Boehm, having lived for years in Boehm's home. In 1882 Schafhäutl wrote a series of articles entitled, "Theobald Boehm: The Life of a Remarkable Artist," which appeared in the *Allgemeine Musikalische Zeitung* of Leipzig. A translation of this life of Boehm is given in Welch's "History of the Boehm Flute," and fills 102 pages. Welch also gives a "Memoir of Dr. Schafhäutl" which fills 24 pages.

In 1909, as stated in the Preface, the translator received from Mr. James S. Wilkins, Jr., an account of Boehm's life-work written by Mr. Wilkins in 1900. This gives the impressions of Boehm's personal characteristics as received by an American pupil who was closely associated with Boehm for more than three years, and it also gives some opinions expressed by Boehm which have not been found elsewhere. Extracts from this account are therefore given here; the parts omitted are mostly descriptions of Boehm's experiments and conclusions which are given by Boehm himself in this treatise, and accounts of his work in connection with the iron and steel industry, which are given in full by Schafhäutl.

THEOBALD BOEHM—AN APPRECIATION
by
JAMES S. WILKINS, JR.
1900

It was the good fortune of the writer to become the pupil of Theobald Boehm in May, 1871, and to enjoy the inestimable honor of being made a close friend and companion by him for more than three years.

During the writer's sojourn in Munich, he translated into English Mr. Boehm's work on the flute, "Die Flöte und das Flötenspiel" (which remained in Boehm's possession, unpublished). It was suggested at this time that Mr. Boehm's biography would be of interest as an introduction to the translation, but he was opposed to this. His life was devoted to study and investigation, carried out in the systematic manner so characteristic of the German student and scholar. He was naturally modest and of a retiring nature; his was a character that could not tolerate superficiality or ostentation.

It is only with a desire to give to the lovers of the flute and to admirers of the man who created such a revolution in the instrument, a clearer understanding of the one who has accomplished this result, and to set forth the character of this truly great man, that this sketch of his life is now written.

* * *

Mr. Boehm was about 5 feet, 10 inches in height, of well knit frame and strong constitution. His eyes were a striking feature; they were brown in color, of a wonderful brightness and intelligence, and beaming with kindness. He was full of genial, quiet humor, but with the air of energy and determination which his life bore out. He was highly cultured and had a fund of interesting reminiscence rarely met with.

He was ever ready to encourage the ambitious scholar with advice and assistance, and he did so in a manner to win him the admiration, love, and respect of all with whom he came in contact. It was instinctive with him to bring out all the best qualities of his pupils. His was a great nature—full of charity and human kindness.

As an illustration of Mr. Boehm's method I may give a personal incident. I learned to play all of Boehm's compositions in concert, from memory; in fact, at the close of my three years of study with him, I had a repertoire of 500 solos, memorized! I went to 20 *Altheimereck* every day, at 9 o'clock, a. m., Mr. Boehm would say to me: "I have a new piece"—placing it on the music stand and giving *tempo*—"play it." When I had finished the last page, he would turn the music upside down, and repeat: "Play it." This meant that I should play all that I could remember. In this way I became able to memorize a piece at first reading, and it also taught me to read many bars ahead.

Mr. Boehm's school of tone stands supreme, and his pupils have demonstrated this fact. With him tone was of the first importance, all else became secondary; and, while the development of tone meant drudgery, yet the results compensated for all the labor entailed.

* * *

All this time the natural obstacles to the creation of a perfect flute confronted Mr. Boehm. The human hands have but ten fingers and the musical scale has thirteen tones, and the proper operation of the flute could only be accomplished by mechanical means. For years Mr. Boehm labored on this problem and the hundreds of designs he made in experimentation can hardly be realized. He continued the experiments until he reluctantly decided that any device that could be created for an ideal flute would be so complicated and so subject to disarrangement that it would be impractical. The present flute is not perfect, and Mr. Boehm fully realized this fact. The creation of a mechanism of easy and simple operation, the adoption of dimensions best suited to the scope of the instrument required that some of the tone-holes be located out of their correct acoustical positions. They were established only by experiment. It is impossible to have an adequate realization of the immense amount of labor Mr. Boehm devoted to the determination of such proportions as have given us the wonderful flute that we now have. None but a person of his character would have devoted a life-time to the accomplishment of his ideals.

The writer with the approval of Mr. Boehm worked nine months in his flute factory and learned the practical making of the instrument. Consequently he had many conversations with his preceptor on the reasons that influenced him to establish the present construction of the flute as the most feasible. One of the greatest difficulties he had to contend with was the opposition that players of the old flute had to any innovation or change.

* * *

The tone-holes of wooden flutes are smaller than those made of metal, because of the counter-boring for the pad seats in the former, while the metal flutes have raised edges around the holes. The ideal flute is one of wood with raised tone-holes. The wood of the main part of the tube being cut away for lightness; this permits using full-sized tone-holes. Mr. Boehm did make some few flutes of this kind, and they were splendid instruments, but the greatly increased cost and the danger of splitting made them too expensive, and few players appreciated the real advantages to be derived from their use. (The bass flute tube shown in Fig. 31, presented by Mr. Wilkins, shows such a "thinned wood" tube).

* * *

When he was about sixty years of age Mr. Boehm created his *Alt-Flöte in G.* This was the pride of his life, and during the last twenty years of his life he played on this instrument altogether. The principal obstacle to the popularity of this flute is the fact that no music is arranged for it. It is to be regretted that so little is known of this magnificent instrument.

* * *

One of the great drawbacks to the early adoption of the Boehm System by flute players was the changing of the fingering from the old to the new; this was particularly true as regards the closed G♯ key. The fallacy of the closed G♯ key, strange to say, prevails at the present time to no small extent. Even pupils are taught the false fingering by their teachers who happen themselves to use the old style. This was extremely annoying to Mr. Boehm, who remarked: "If a player goes to the trouble of changing his instrument and system of fingering he should not do so in part. The natural action of the pressing down of the finger on a key is to close the key. Then why, when no mechanical reason prevents, should this G♯ key be left to the unreliable force of a spring to close it, when the direct pressure of the finger will act so positively?" In later years Mr. Boehm would not humor this absurd notion and he refused to make the closed G♯ key for any one.

*   *   *

It was always Mr. Boehm's hope that the tone qualities and possibilities of the flute could be realized as part of the orchestral forces. He maintained that the first two octaves contain the true and natural qualities of the instrument. The third octave is always unsatisfactory; it is seldom that a player who has a fine quality of tone in the third octave, has an equally excellent lower tone, and conversely. Therefore it was Mr. Boehm's wish to create an orchestral set of flutes, composed of flutes in G, in C, and in F, each designed to have a compass of two octaves of the ideal tone quality. But as this would increase the number of flute players in the orchestra there is hardly any possibility of its realization; not that it is impossible but because there is a general indifference to the question.

It is evident from the character of the music at present available for the flute, that very little of it is composed with a full comprehension of the character of the instrument. The prevailing music is nearly all of a florid nature, quite foreign to the acoustical quality of the flute. There is no question that the third octave is false and thin as compared with the lower ones, and, in fact, these lower octaves are purposely injured in order to develop the third or artificial octave. (See page 19. These arguments do not apply to the flute in G made on Boehm's dimensions). The proof of this fact is found in the irregular fingering that must be used to produce the third octave. The elimination of the effort to produce three full octaves of tones would permit the development of the full, rich tone of the two lower octaves which give the qualities that tend to make the flute the beautiful instrument that it is. Development along these natural lines is the ideal to be sought.

* * *

Mr. Boehm had seven sons and one daughter, and once when speaking of his family, said: "I have raised a good family and have given them all a good education to fit them to make their way in the world." This was true; one son became Manager of the Bavarian State Railways, another Manager of a locomotive factory, a third Manager of the Stuttgart gas works, one was secretary to Prince Charles, two held positions of trust in municipal offices in Munich, and one carried on the family business of goldsmith and jeweler, all being men of prominent position in their communities. The daughter never married and lived at home.

Mr. Boehm's affliction in later years was the failure of his eye-sight. This was not caused alone by advancing years, but was the result mainly of the years of hard work spent in experiments in making steel from iron directly. The constant watching of the metal and the heat of the intense fires seriously affected his eyes.

* * *

It was remarkable that a man who had been so active as Mr. Boehm had been for many years, should retain his faculties in such a marked degree to the time of his death. In 1872, when he was in his seventy-seventh year, he was as companionable as the average man of sixty years, and his mind was as bright. This was probably due to the well regulated life he led. Until his death, in 1881, he always dwelt upon the improvement of the flute or upon the arrangement of some music for it.

* * *

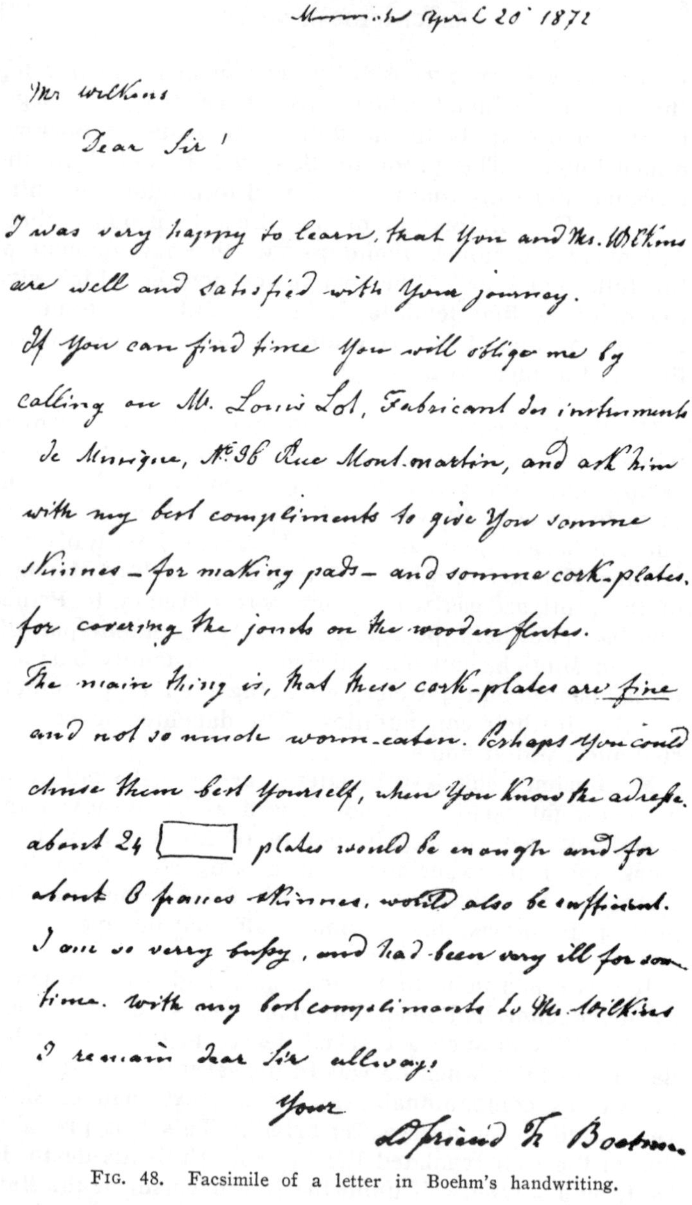

Munich April 20 1872

Mr Wilkins
    Dear Sir!

I was very happy to learn, that You and Mrs. Wilkins
are well and satisfied with Your journey.
If You can find time You will oblige me by
calling on Mr. Louis Lot, Fabricant des instruments
de Musique, No. 36 Rue Mont-martin, and ask him
with my best compliments to give You somme
skinnes _ for making pads _ and somme cork-plates.
for covering the joints on the wooden flutes.
The main thing is, that these cork-plates are fine
and not so much worm-eaten. Perhaps You could
chuse them best Yourself, when You know the adresse.
about 24 [   ] plates would be enough and for
about 8 francs skinnes, would also be sufficient.
I am so verry busy, and had been very ill for some
time. With my best compliments to Mrs. Wilkins
I remain dear Sir allways
              Your
                  old friend Th. Boehm

Fig. 48. Facsimile of a letter in Boehm's handwriting.

A letter written by Boehm to Mr. Wilkins when the latter was visiting Paris, is reproduced in fac-simile on the opposite page. This letter throws an interesting side-light upon Boehm's personal quali-ties. While there are traces of his multi-lingual accomplishments, yet it shows that he was very competent in English composition, and it shows him to be the man of courtesy and culture to which Mr. Wilkins and others have abundantly attested. Mr. Wilkins was accompanied by his mother during his stay in Europe, and it is to her that Boehm refers in the opening and closing sen-tences.

Boehm's researches in acoustics, while mostly applicable to the flute, are fundamental, and they have influenced the development of other wind in-struments with keys, such as the clarinet, oboe, bassoon, etc. Some features of Boehm's key mech-anism are in general use with these instruments, and are referred to by his name. The location of the holes, however, cannot be carried out for these instruments, according to the *Schema,* be-cause of the modifying influence of the reed.

Boehm's attempt, in 1831, to improve the piano-forte shows that he approached the subject in a thoroughly rational manner; his method was cor-rect, and is now universally adopted; he failed temporarily, because he had no facilities to carry on the work. The *Encyclopaedia Britannica,* 11th edition, article "Pianoforte," says, "The first sug-gestion for the overstringing in the piano, was made by the celebrated flute-player and inventor

Theobald Boehm, who carried it beyond theory in London, in 1831, by employing a small firm located in Cheapside, Gerock & Wolf, to make some overstrung pianos for him. Boehm expected to gain in tone. Pape, an ingenious mechanician in Paris, tried a like experiment to gain economy in dimensions. Tomkinson in London continued Pape's model, but neither Boehm's nor Pape's took permanent root. Later in 1855, Henry Engelhard Steinway, who had emigrated from Brunswick to New York in 1849, and had established the firm of Steinway & Sons in 1853 in that city, effected a combination of an overstrung scale with the American iron frame * * * leading ultimately to important results. The Chickering firm claim to have anticipated the Steinways in this invention."

Boehm devised a new method of transmitting rotatory motion. A model of this was presented before the Society of Arts, Manufactures and Commerce, of London, and on June 8, 1835, the president of the Society, the Duke of Sussex, presented Boehm with the Silver Medal of the Society. The record is found in the *Transactions* of the Society, Vol. L, Part II, for the Session 1834-35, pages 82 and 83. It begins as follows: "Method of Communicating Rotatory Motion. The Silver Medal was presented to Mr. Theobald Boehm, member of the Royal Chapel at Munich, in Bavaria, for his Method of Communicating Rotatory Motion; a Model of which has been placed in the Society's Repository. The usual modes of communicating rotatory motion from the first mover, are by means either of wheels and pinions, or of two plane cylinders connected by a band. Mr. Boehm has suggested another method, described in the annexed figures." Then follows a technical description of the figures; these figures are reproduced in Fig. 49, from which the nature of the device can be easily inferred, without further description.

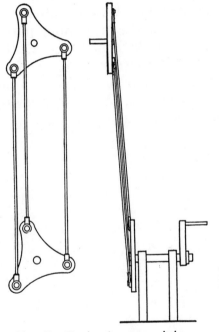

FIG. 49. Device for transmitting
rotatory motion.

Boehm received many medals, decorations, and prizes. Mr. Welch says: "So many prize medals and similar distinctions did he succeed in obtaining, that he had a drawer specially devoted to them. The old man seemed quite pleased when, only a few weeks before his death, he opened it and showed me his trophies." He received three Grand First Prize Gold Medals for his flutes, at the London Exhibition of 1851, at the German Industrial Exhibition, Munich, in 1854, and at the Paris Exhibition of 1855. In 1835 he was awarded the Silver Medal of the Society of Arts of London for the method of transmitting rotatory motion, described in the preceding paragraph. In 1839 the King of Bavaria bestowed the Cross of the Knights of the Order of Merit of St. Michael, for Boehm's introduction into the iron-works of Bavaria of improved puddling processes for the manufacture of steel.

PREIS-COURANT

von

Theobald Böhm & Mendler in München.

		Mark	Pf
No. I.	Eine Silberflöte (in C) mit Embouchure von Gold	410	—
	Dito mit H-Fuss	450	—
II.	Flöte von Cocus- oder Grenadille-Holz mit Silber	375	—
	Dito mit H-Fuss	410	—
„ III.	Holzflöte mit Neusilber	300	—
„ IV.	Flöte von Neusilber mit Holz-Embouchure		
„ V.	Eine Altflöte (in G) von Silber mit Gold-Embouchure	630	—
	Dito von Neusilber mit Holz-Embouchure	450	—
„ VI.	Piccolo von Silber mit Holz-Embouchure	300	—
	Dito von Holz mit Silber	250	—
	Dito von Holz mit Neusilber		

Zu den Flöten No. I und II wird auf Verlangen noch gemacht:

	Mark	Pf
a) Ein Trillerhebel zur $\overset{2}{C}$-Klappe	24	—
*b) Eine Schleifklappe	18	—
c) Federn von Gold	18	—

Requisiten:	Mark	Pf
Eine Garnitur Klappenpolster	3	—
Schraubenzieher und Federnhäckchen	3	—
Stopselmass	1	—
Grifftabelle	3	—
Emballage mit Holzkistchen	2	—

Bemerkungen. * Mittelst der sehr bequemen Schleifklappe können die Töne:
$\overset{2}{dis}$-$\overset{1}{es}$, $\overset{3}{d}$, $\overset{3}{dis}$-$\overset{3}{es}$, $\overset{3}{e}$, $\overset{3}{a}$ und $\overset{3}{b}$, auch im Pianissimo vollkommen rein und
sicher gespielt werden.

Versendungen werden nur gegen erfolgte Baarzahlungen oder Wechsel
auf bekannte deutsche Bankhäuser gemacht.

FIG. 50. A facsimile of Boehm and Mendler's Price List of Flutes, of
the year 1877.

(b) Descriptive Price List of Boehm & Mendler Flutes

The manuscript copy of "Die Flöte und das Flötenspiel" concludes with a descriptive catalogue of the various styles of flutes manufactured by Boehm & Mendler. This part, however, has been crossed out, indicating Boehm's decision not to publish it. In the translator's collection there are several of the original price-lists of Boehm & Mendler and of Carl Mendler; a photographic reproduction of one of these is shown in Fig. 50. This was sent, in 1877, by Boehm himself to Mr. Chaffee of Detroit, who purchased the flute described in the Group, Fig. 31, No. 11. Shafhäutl's "Life of Boehm," in the German edition, gives a catalogue, which is much the same as Boehm's list, except that it is more detailed and is expressed in language almost naïve. Since the English version of Schafhäutl's "Life" does not contain this matter, it is given below, with the addition of a few minor items for the sake of completeness, taken from a Carl Mendler price-list.

Herr Carl Mendler, who took over Boehm's flute-making establishment in 1862, continues the manufacture of the Boehm flutes in all their newest developments.

A flute in C of cocus or grenadilla wood with silver keys is provided for 375 marks. If one wishes a B♮ foot-joint, the price is increased to 410 marks; while if the foot descends only to D♮ the price of the flute is but 320 marks.

With this flute there is furnished an elegant case, which contains not only the flute, but also the necessary tools with which to take the flute apart when the mechanism needs cleaning, or a key pad needs changing, or, perchance, to remedy some disturbance in the operation of the mechanism. These requisites consist of: one set of key pads, 3 marks; a screw driver with a spring hook, 3 marks; a stopper measure by which the cork can be replaced in the correct position, 1 mark; tables of fingerings, 3 marks; cost of packing the flute in a wooden box, 2 marks. These items together amount to 12 marks.

An extra foot-joint to B♮ costs 95 marks, one to C costs 65 marks, and one to D♮ only costs 30 marks. An extra head-joint of silver or of wood costs 50 marks.

A flute in C, of silver with gold embouchure, costs 410 marks. The same instrument with a B♮ foot-joint is 450 marks, or with a D♮ foot it is 360 marks.

The same flute of the newest system with a large diameter of bore, 20 millimeters, giving a fuller tone, with a foot to C, costs 485 marks, or with a foot to B♮ the price is 525 marks.

There is still Boehm's latest improvement, the above silver flute of 20 millimeters bore with a head-joint of grenadilla wood, the price of which is 475 marks with a C foot, or 515 marks with a B♮ foot. By means of this head-joint of wood, the flute acquires the character of tone of the wood flute.

In accordance with the old system of flute, and especially to conform to the French style, there will be supplied, instead of the Boehm open G♯ key, a closed G♯ key at an extra cost of 20 marks. One may also have a trill lever for the C key (thumb key) which can be played by the first finger of the right hand; Mendler furnishes this for 24 marks.

Mendler also provides his flutes with the octave-key by which certain tones can easily and surely be produced in *pianissimo*. The price of this is 18 marks.

If one wishes gold springs instead of steel springs, the extra cost is 18 marks. And little gold plates may be put on the keys where the fingers press, for 50 marks.

A flute of cocus or grenadilla wood with keys of German silver, with steel springs, open G♯ key and C foot, costs 300 marks; with B♮ foot, 320 marks, and with foot to D♮, 270 marks.

A bass flute in G (Alt-Flöte) of silver with a gold embouchure costs 650 marks. A similar flute of German silver with an embouchure of wood costs only 450 marks.

A piccolo of silver with embouchure of wood costs 300 marks, while the price of a piccolo made of cocus or grenadilla wood, with keys of silver, is 250 marks.

Unless it is otherwise desired, all of these flutes are provided with the thumb rest (the crutch for the left hand).

These prices may seem high; however, it is not possible, because of the complicated and delicate mechanism, to secure its accurate working by means of the cheaper workmanship. The correct adjustment of this complicated mechanism requires the skill of an exceptional mechanic. Boehm had at one time a mechanic from the celebrated workshop of Ertel, but his work was not sufficiently accurate. The same was the case with a mechanic from the celebrated optical establishment of Merz.

It was not until the year 1854, when the present proprietor of the factory, the exceptionally skilled watchmaker, Carl Mendler, became foreman, that it was possible to make the mechanism of the required perfection.

Flutes on Boehm's system are to be found in the market at cheaper prices; but one must not be misled; the closing of the keys, for example, will be very imperfect, or the flute itself will be unmanageable, and the instrument will be found more often in the hands of the repairer than in those of the artist.

(c) List of Boehm's Compositions

Schafhäutl in his "Life of Boehm" (Welch: "History of the Boehm Flute"), gives a list of Boehm's compositions, prepared from his personal papers. In this list there are numerous errors and omissions. The translator's collection contains copies, in the original editions, of all of Boehm's published compositions and arrangements (excepting Op. 14). The following list gives the complete titles as they appear on the printed music. Wherever this list differs from that of Schafhäutl and Welch this one may be taken as correct. In the absence of other information, Schafhäutl has been followed.

Schafhäutl, in the German edition, gives the following sentences as an introduction to the List of Compositions: "In order that our picture of the man whose methods and works we have followed through various fields of human endeavor, may be made complete and well filled-out, we must also keep in view the man as an artist in his creations. From his first composition, which appeared in the year 1822, to his last which was published in 1881, there flows continuously the living spirit; and even in the most difficult etudes for the virtuoso there is always a vivifying musical thought. Throughout all of his many-sided compositions for the flute, we find that he holds truly and steadfastly to an aesthetic unity which gives them an enduring value."

When a title in the following list is followed by an asterisk, *, it signifies that there is an accompaniment for the pianoforte; two asterisks, **, signify an accompaniment for the pianoforte and also for the orchestra; the obelisk, †, indicates that the accompaniment is for the orchestra only; the absence of a mark indicates that the composition is for the flute alone.

I.   ORIGINAL COMPOSITIONS WITH OPUS NUMBERS

Opus	Date	Title	Key	
1	1822	Concerto pour la Flûte, dédié à Monsieur A. B. Fürstenau ____	G maj.	* *
2		La Sentinelle Air Favori Varié dédié a son Elève Monsieur Guillaume Zink _____	G maj.	* *
3		Andante und Polonaise_____ _____A maj. and	D maj.	* *
4		Nel cor più non mi sento, thême varié _____	G maj.	* *
5		P o t p o u r i sur des Mélodies Suisses, Duo concertant _____	G maj.	*
6		Divertissement sur un Air de Caraffa, dédié à Monsieur de Manostetter _____	G maj.	* *
7		Concertante pour deux Flûtes, (with orchestral accompaniment only) _____	G maj.	†
8		Polonaise de Caraffa _____	D maj.	* *
9		Variations sur un thême de l'Opera: Robin-de-Bois (Der Freyschütz) de Weber, dédiées à son ami Fr. Hoffmann_____	D maj.	* *
10		Divertissement sur un thême favori de Rovelli dédié à Monsieur Krüger _____	D maj.	* *
11		Divertissement sur deux thêmes favoris suisses _____C maj. and	G maj.	* *
12		Rondo Brilliant, dédié à Son Ami Charles Keller, (with orchestral accompaniment only)	D maj.	†

13		Divertissement sur l'air favori intitulé Almalied, par Baron de Poissl introduit dans l'Opera Donauweibchen, dédié à Son Eleve Monsieur David Marx _____	G maj.	* *
14		"Boehm et Ogden." Fantaisie concert sur un thême ecossais	D maj.	*
15		12 Etudes pour la Flûte, propres à égaliser le doigté dans toutes les gammes _____		
16		Grande Polonaise, dediée à Monsieur Camus _____	D maj.	* *
17		Variations sur la marche de l'Opera Moisé, dediées à Monsieur Tulou _____	D maj.	* *
18		I—Erstes Walzer Potpourri, nach Franz Schubert'schen und anderen beliebten Motiven _____	(various)	*
		II—Andante und Polonaise nach Motiven von Caraffa. Dedicated to Mr. Alfred Croshaw Johnson _____	(various)	*
19		Choix d'Airs de l'Opera "Macbeth" par A. H. Chelard_____		*
20	1838	Variations sur un Air Tyrolien (Swiss Boy) dédiées à Monsieur Prosper Amtmann_____	C maj.	* *
21	1838	Fantaisie sur un air de Beethoven. (Sehnsuchtswalzer) ___	Ab maj.	* *
22	1840	Variations brillantes sur l'air allemand "Du, du liegst mir im Herzen" _____	E maj.	* *
23	1845	Fantaisie sur des thêmes suisses. dediée à Mr. J. Clinton_____	F maj.	* *
24	1845	Fantaisie sur des thêmes suisses dediée à Mr. L. Dorus _____	E maj.	* *
25	1852	Fantaisie sur des airs écossais	C maj.	* *
26	1852	Twenty-four Capricios, dedicated to Edward Jekyll, Esqre.		
27	1853	Souvenir des Alpes; I. Andante cantabile _____	Eb maj.	*

28	1853	Souvenir des Alpes; II. Rondo-Allegro _ _ _ _ _ _ _ _ _ _ _ _ _ _ _ _ _	C maj.	*
29	1853	Souvenir des Alpes; III. Andantino, Romance _ _ _ _ _ _ _ _ _ _ _ _	D maj.	*
30	1853	Souvenir des Alpes; IV. Rondo-Allegretto _ _ _ _ _ _ _ _ _ _ _ _ _ _	D maj.	*
31	1853	Souvenir des Alpes; V. Andante pastorale _ _ _ _ _ _ _ _ _ _ _ _ _ _	G maj.	*
32	1853	Souvenir des Alpes; VI. Rondo-Ländler _ _ _ _ _ _ _ _ _ _ _ _ _ _ _	E maj.	*
33	1858	Andante _ _ _ _ _ _ _ _ _ _ _ _ _ _ _ _ _	B maj.	*
34	1859	A la Tarantella, dediée à Monsieur Antoine Sacchetti_ _ _ _ _ _	E min.	*
35	1859	Larghetto, dedié à Monsieur Louis Dorus _ _ _ _ _ _ _ _ _ _ _ _ _	A♭ maj.	*
36	1859	Rondo à la Mazurka _ _ _ _ _ _ _ _ _ _ _	C maj.	*
37	1863	24 Etudes, avec accomp. de Piano. En 4 Suites _ _ _ _ _ _ _ _		*
38				
39				
40				
41				
42				
43				
44				
45	1876	Fantasie über Motive einer Sonate von F. H. Himmel, à Hernn Camille Thierry_ _ _ _ _ _	C maj.	*
		(This work appears as No. 12 in the list, II, of "Compositionen berühmter Meister," and bears the opus number on the first page of music and not on the title page.)		
46	1880	Andante aus der Serenade, Op. 25, von L. van Beethoven. To Herrn Eugen Weiner in New York _ _ _ _ _ _ _ _ _ _ _ _ _ _ _ _ _	G maj.	*
47	1881	Elégie, dediée à Monsieur le Dr. F. Jsenschmid _ _ _ _ _ _ _ _ _ _ _	A♭ maj.	* *

1-13   Vollständige Sammlung der Con-
            cert Compositionen für die
            Flöte mit Hinweglassung der
            Begleitung.   (Contains solo
            parts only of Op. 1 to 13 in-
            clusive, with the exception of
            Op. 5.)

II. TRANSCRIPTIONS WITHOUT OPUS NUMBERS

This group of transcriptions for the flute and piano appears under the general title: *Compositionen berühmter Meister.*

No.	Date	Title	Key	
1	1872	Adagio, (Largo, Pianoforte Concerto, Op. 15), von L. v. Beethoven ---------------	C maj.	*
2	1872	Adagio, von Mozart. Aus der Clavier-Sonate Op. 16--------	B♭ maj.	*
3	1872	Rondo-Andante von Mozart----	A min.	*
4	1872	Ständchen. Lied von Franz Schubert -------------------	D min.	*
5	1872	Das Fischermädchen. Lied von Franz Schubert ------------	D maj.	*
6	1872	Tre giorni. Aria von Pergolese	C min.	*
7	1872	Cantabile von Vogler----------	D maj.	*
8	1872	Aria cantabile von J. S. Bach---	D maj.	*
9	1876	Marcia, Adagio, Menuetto, Allegretto alla Polacca und Tema con Variazioni aus L. v. Beethoven's Serenade Op. 8. (Original for Violin, Viola and Violincello.) Gerwidmit Herrn M. Schweninger ------------	D maj.	*
10	1876	Romanze von L. v. Beethoven, Op. 50 --------------------	F maj.	*
11	1876	Variationen von Haydn über das Thema: Gott erhalte Franz den Kaiser -----------------	G maj.	*

(The List printed on the cover of the music of this series contains twelve numbers, but No. 12 is clearly marked "Opus 45," and is now entered in group I only.)

III. MISCELLANEOUS WORKS WITHOUT NUMBERS

There is no available record of the titles to which Boehm intended to attach the seven opus numbers from 38 to 44, inclusive. There remain just seven published works which bear no opus or serial numbers, and whose dates of publication correspond with those appropriate to the missing opera. It is suggested that these works are the ones which should bear the opus numbers from 38 to 44, inclusive:

No.	Opus	Date	Title	Key	
1	(38)	1863	Andante de Mozart, Op. 86. (Arranged from the original MS. score, for the flute and piano, and for the flute in G and piano)	C maj.	*
2	(39)	1868	Arie aus Orpheus: "Che faro senza Euridice," von Gluck. Au Colonel Comte A. Vargas de Bedemar _____	E♭ maj.	*
3	(40)	1868	Cujus Animam. Célèbre Air du Stabat Mater de Rossini. Dedié à Mr. Hermann Kohlke _____	A♭ maj.	*
4	(41)	1871	12 Uebungstücke für die Flöte zur Erlangung einer gleichmässigen Fingerbewegung in allen Tonarten. Zugleich als Anhang zu dessen theor. Werke: Die Flöte und das Flötenspiel in akustischer, technischer und artistischer Beziehung__		
5	(42)	1876	Adagio aus dem Quintetto für Clarinette von Mozart _____	G maj.	*
6	(43)		3 Duos pour deux Flûtes tirés des oeuvres de F. Mendelssohn Bartholdy et de Fr. Lachner. No. 1. Sur Melodies de Mendelssohn _____	B♭ maj.	*

No. 2. Sur Melodies de Mendelssohn _____	Eb maj.	*
No. 3. Sur Melodies de Lachner _____	F maj.	*

(This series of three duets, published in Paris, is clearly marked "Opus 33." Possibly this is a misprint for "Opus 43.")

7 (44) "My Native Home." (Sehnsucht nach dem Rigi.) Song with flute obbligato.

IV. UNPUBLISHED ARRANGEMENTS FOR THE FLUTE IN G

There is no evidence that there are any unpublished original compositions by Boehm. The group of pieces listed below consists of arrangements with parts for the flute in G. In nearly all of the numbers, the "arrange-ment" seemingly required is merely the transposition of a part into a suitable key for the flute in G. The list is very interesting as indicating the selections which Boehm had found especially adapted to this instrument. The publication of these works at the present time, in "album" form, might stimulate the interest in this beauti-ful instrument.

The keys in this list are those given by Schafhäutl. These would indicate that in some instances the solo part has been transposed, while in other cases it is the ac-companiment that has been rewritten. Twelve of the numbers seem to be the same compositions as are repre-sented by twelve of the published works; the numbers in parenthesis refer to the corresponding groups and num-bers.

FOR FLUTE IN G AND PIANOFORTE

No.	Title	Key
1	Beethoven. Adagio. Largo from the Piano-forte Concerto, Op. 15. (II-1) _____	Ab maj.
2	Beethoven. Sonata, Op. 17. The original for Horn and Pianoforte _____	F maj.
3	Beethoven. Serenade, Op. 25. The original for Flute, Violin and Viola. (I-Op. 46) ___	
4	Haydn. Variations on "God Preserve the Emperor." The original for String Quar-tette. (II-11) _____	

5 Himmel. Rondo. From a Sonata originally for Flute and Pianoforte. (I-Op. 45, and II-12) _____ G maj.

6 Mozart. Adagio. From the Pianoforte Sonata, Op. 16. (II-2) _____ Bb maj.

7 Mozart. Rondo Andante, Op. 71. The original for the Pianoforte alone. (II-3) _____

8 Mozart. Sonata. The original for Violin and Pianoforte _____ G maj.

9 Mozart. Adagio from the Clarinet Quintette. (III-5) _____ D maj.

10 Schubert. Song: "Das Ständchen." (Serenade.) (II-5) _____ D min.

11 Schubert. Song: "Das Fischermädchen." (II-5) _____ A maj.

12 Schubert. Song: "Am Meer." _____ C maj.

13 Vogler. Cantabile. Adagio from an Organ Prelude. (II-7) _____ D min.

DUETS FOR FLUTE IN G AND FLUTE IN C, WITH PIANOFORTE

14 Rossini. Duo: Soirées Musicales _____ A maj.

15 Rossini. Duo: Soirées Musicales _____ D maj.

16 Weber. Romance _____ F maj.

17 Weber. Andantino _____ C maj.

18 Weber. Allegretto _____ C maj.

TRIOS FOR FLUTE IN G AND TWO FLUTES IN C

19 Beethoven. Trio, Op. 87. The original for two Oboes and Cor Anglais _____ F maj.

20 Vogler. Cantabile. Adagio from an Organ Prelude. (II-7, and IV-6) _____ D maj.

FOR FLUTE IN G AND SOPRANO VOICE, WITH ACCOMPANIMENT

21 Scheidemayer. Graduale. With Latin text for church use, and also with German text. With Pianoforte accompaniment_____ C maj.

22 Walter. Graduale. For Solo Flute in G, Vocal Quartette, and accompaniment for two Violins, Viola, Cello and Bass_____ E maj.

(d) BIBLIOGRAPHY

There follows a very brief and incomplete list of current books relating to the flute. Older treatises of historical value, instructors, books of music, and books treating of musical instruments in general have not been included. More extended bibliographies are given by Rockstro, Welch, and Fitzgibbon, in the works mentioned below.

BOEHM, THEOBALD.—An Essay on the Construction of Flutes. Edited by W. S. Broadwood. This book is Boehm's own English version of his treatise of 1847, *Ueber den Flötenbau und die neuesten Verbesserungen desselben*, to which the editor has added an account of the *Schema*, and numerous letters of interest. London: Rudall, Carte & Co., 1882. Octavo, X + 78 pages.

ROCKSTRO, R. S.—A Treatise on the Construction, the History, and the Practice of the Flute. London: Rudall, Carte & Co., 1890. Octavo, XLII + 664 pages.

WELCH, CHRISTOPHER.—History of the Boehm Flute, with Schafhäutl's Life of Boehm. London: Rudall, Carte & Co.; New York, G. Schirmer; 3rd edition, 1896. Octavo, XXIII + 504 pages.

FITZGIBBON, H. MACAULAY.—The Story of the Flute. London, Walter Scott Publishing Co.; New York, Charles Scribner's Sons. 1914. Duodecimo, XVI + 292 pages.

WELCH, CHRISTOPHER.—Six Lectures on the Recorder and Other Flutes in Relation to Literature. London: Oxford University Press, 1911. Octavo, XVI + 457 pages.

EHRLICH, D.—The History of the Flute. New York: D. Ehrlich, 1921. Duodecimo, XI + 107 pages.

SCHWEDLER, MAXIMILIAN.—Katechismus der Flöte und des Flötenspiels. Leipzig: J. J. Weber, 3rd edition, 1914. Sexto-decimo, 112 pages and tables.

SQUARZONI, FRANCESCO.—Il Flauto, Cenno Storico. Ferrara, Italia, G. Bresciani. 1917. Octavo, 48 pages.

THE FLUTIST.—A monthly magazine devoted exclusively to the flute and flute playing. It is of interest and value, alike to the professional and the amateur flutist. Edited and published by EMIL MEDICUS, Asheville, North Carolina.

INDEX

CATALOG OF DOVER BOOKS

Music

A GENERAL HISTORY OF MUSIC, Charles Burney. A detailed coverage of music from the Greeks up to 1789, with full information on all types of music: sacred and secular, vocal and instrumental, operatic and symphonic. Theory, notation, forms, instruments, innovators, composers, performers, typical and important works, and much more in an easy, entertaining style. Burney covered much of Europe and spoke with hundreds of authorities and composers so that this work is more than a compilation of records . . . it is a living work of careful and first-hand scholarship. Its account of thoroughbass (18th century) Italian music is probably still the best introduction on the subject. A recent NEW YORK TIMES review said, "Surprisingly few of Burney's statements have been invalidated by modern research . . . still of great value." Edited and corrected by Frank Mercer. 35 figures. Indices. 1915pp. 5⅜ x 8. 2 volumes. **T36 The Set, Clothbound $12.50**

A DICTIONARY OF HYMNOLOGY, John Julian. This exhaustive and scholarly work has become known as an invaluable source of hundreds of thousands of important and often difficult to obtain facts on the history and use of hymns in the western world. Everyone interested in hymns will be fascinated by the accounts of famous hymns and hymn writers and amazed by the amount of practical information he will find. More than 30,000 entries on individual hymns, giving authorship, date and circumstances of composition, publication, textual variations, translations, denominational and ritual usage, etc. Biographies of more than 9,000 hymn writers, and essays on important topics such as Christmas carols and children's hymns, and much other unusual and valuable information. A 200 page double-columned index of first lines — the largest in print. Total of 1786 pages in two reinforced clothbound volumes. 6¼ x 9¼. **The set, T333 Clothbound $15.00**

MUSIC IN MEDIEVAL BRITAIN, F. Ll. Harrison. The most thorough, up-to-date, and accurate treatment of the subject ever published, beautifully illustrated. Complete account of institutions and choirs; carols, masses, and motets; liturgy and plainsong; and polyphonic music from the Norman Conquest to the Reformation. Discusses the various schools of music and their reciprocal influences; the origin and development of new ritual forms; development and use of instruments; and new evidence on many problems of the period. Reproductions of scores, over 200 excerpts from medieval melodies. Rules of harmony and dissonance; influence of Continental styles; great composers (Dunstable, Cornysh, Fairfax, etc.); and much more. Register and index of more than 400 musicians. Index of titles. General Index. 225-item bibliography. 6 Appendices. xix + 491pp. 5⅝ x 8¾. **T705 Clothbound $10.00**

THE MUSIC OF SPAIN, Gilbert Chase. Only book in English to give concise, comprehensive account of Iberian music; new Chapter covers music since 1941. Victoria, Albéniz, Cabezón, Pedrell, Turina, hundreds of other composers; popular and folk music; the Gypsies; the guitar; dance, theatre, opera, with only extensive discussion in English of the Zarzuela; virtuosi such as Casals; much more. "Distinguished . . . readable," Saturday Review. 400-item bibliography. Index. 27 photos. 383pp. 5⅜ x 8. **T549 Paperbound $2.00**

ON STUDYING SINGING, Sergius Kagen. An intelligent method of voice-training, which leads you around pitfalls that waste your time, money, and effort. Exposes rigid, mechanical systems, baseless theories, deleterious exercises. "Logical, clear, convincing . . . dead right," Virgil Thomson, N.Y. Herald Tribune. "I recommend this volume highly," Maggie Teyte, Saturday Review. 119pp. 5⅜ x 8. **T622 Paperbound $1.25**

WILLIAM LAWES, M. Lefkowitz. This is the definitive work on Lawes, the versatile, prolific, and highly original "King's musician" of 17th century England. His life is reconstructed from original documents, and nearly every piece he ever wrote is examined and evaluated: his fantasias, pavans, violin "sonatas," lyra viol and bass viol suites, and music for harp and theorbo; and his songs, masques, and theater music to words by Herrick ("Gather Ye Rosebuds"), Jonson, Suckling, Shirley, and others. The author shows the innovations of dissonance, augmented triad, and other Italian influences Lawes helped introduce to England. List of Lawes' complete works and several complete scores by this major precursor of Purcell and the 18th century developments. Index. 5 Appendices. 52 musical excerpts, many never before in print. Bibliography. x + 320pp. 5⅜ x 8. **T706 Clothbound $10.00**

THE FUGUE IN BEETHOVEN'S PIANO MUSIC, J. V. Cockshoot. The first study of a neglected aspect of Beethoven's genius: his ability as a writer of fugues. Analyses of early studies and published works demonstrate his original and powerful contributions to composition. 34 works are examined, with 143 musical excerpts. For all pianists, teachers, students, and music-minded readers with a serious interest in Beethoven. Index. 93-item bibliography. Illustration of original score for "Fugue in C." xv + 212pp. 5⅝ x 8⅜. **T704 Clothbound $6.00**

CATALOGUE OF DOVER BOOKS

JOHANN SEBASTIAN BACH, Philipp Spitta. The complete and unabridged text of the definitive study of Bach. Written some 70 years ago, it is still unsurpassed for its coverage of nearly all aspects of Bach's life and work. There could hardly be a finer non-technical introduction to Bach's music than the detailed, lucid analyses which Spitta provides for hundreds of individual pieces. 26 solid pages are devoted to the B minor mass, for example, and 30 pages to the glorious St. Matthew Passion. This monumental set also includes a major analysis of the music of the 18th century: Buxtehude, Pachelbel, etc. "Unchallenged as the last word on one of the supreme geniuses of music," John Barkham, SATURDAY REVIEW SYNDICATE. Total of 1819pp. 2 volumes. Heavy cloth binding. 5⅜ x 8. T252 The set, Clothbound **$12.50**

THE LIFE OF MOZART, O. Jahn. Probably the largest amount of material on Mozart's life and works ever gathered together in one book! Its 1350 authoritative and readable pages cover every event in his life, and contain a full critique of almc t every piece he ever wrote, including sketches and intimate works. There is a full historical-cultural background, and vast research into musical and literary history, sources of librettos, prior treatments of Don Juan legend, etc. This is the complete and unaltered text of the definitive Townsend translation, with foreword by Grove. 5 engraved portraits from Salzburg archives. 4 facsimiles in Mozart's hand. 226 musical examples. 4 Appendixes, including complete list of Mozart's compositions, with Köchel numbers (fragmentary works included). Total of xxviii + 1352pp. Three volume set. 5⅜ x 8.
T85 Vol. I Clothbound **$5.00**
T86 Vol. II Clothbound **$5.00**
The set **$10.00**

BEETHOVEN'S QUARTETS, J. de Marliave. The most complete and authoritative study ever written, enjoyable for scholar and layman alike. The 16 quartets and Grand Fugue are all analyzed bar by bar and theme by theme, not over-technically, but concentrating on mood and effects. Complete background material for each composition: influences, first reviews, etc. Preface by Gabriel Fauré. Introduction and notes by J. Escarra. Translated by Hilda Andrews. 321 musical examples. xxiii + 379pp. 5⅜ x 8. T694 Paperbound **$1.85**

STRUCTURAL HEARING: TONAL COHERENCE IN MUSIC, Felix Salzer. Written by a pupil of the late Heinrich Schenker, this is not only the most thorough exposition in English of the Schenker method but also extends the Schenker approach to include modern music, the middle ages, and renaissance music. It explores the phenomenon of tonal organization by means of a detailed analysis and discussion of more than 500 musical pieces. It casts new light for the reader acquainted with harmony upon the understanding of musical compositions, problems of musical coherence, and connection between theory and composition. "Has been the foundation on which all teaching in music theory has been based at this college," Leopold Mannes, President of The Mannes College of Music. 2 volumes. Total of 658pp. 6½ x 9¼.
The set, T418 Clothbound **$8.00**

ANTONIO STRADIVARI: HIS LIFE AND WORK (1644-1737), W. Henry Hill, Arthur F. Hill, and Alfred E. Hill. Still the only book that really delves into life and art of the incomparable Italian craftsman, maker of the finest musical instruments in the world today. The authors, expert violin-makers themselves, discuss Stradivari's ancestry, his construction and finishing techniques, distinguished characteristics of many of his instruments and their locations. Included, too, is story of introduction of his instruments into France, England, first revelation of their supreme merit, and information on his labels, number of instruments made, prices, mystery of ingredients of his varnish, tone of pre-1684 Stradivari violin and changes between 1684 and 1690. An extremely interesting, informative account for all music lovers, from craftsman to concert-goer. Republication of original (1902) edition. New introduction by Sydney Beck, Head of Rare Book and Manuscript Collections, Music Division, New York Public Library. Analytical index by Rembert Wurlitzer. Appendixes. 68 illustrations. 30 full-page plates. 4 in color. xxvi + 315pp. 5⅜ x 8½. T425 Paperbound **$2.25**

THREE CLASSICS IN THE AESTHETIC OF MUSIC, Claude Debussy, Ferrucio Busoni, and Charles Ives. Three very different points of view by three top-ranking modern composers. "M. Croche, the Dilettante-Hater" consists of twenty-five brief articles written by Debussy between the years 1901 and 1905, a sparkling collection of personal commentary on a wide range of topics. Busoni's "Toward a New Aesthetic of Music" considers the nature of absolute music in an attempt to suggest answers to the question, What are the aims of music?, and discusses modern systems of tonality and harmony, the concept of unity of keys, etc. Ives's "Essays Before a Sonata," a literary complement to the movements of the author's "Concord, 1845" piano sonata, contains his most mature analysis of his art. Stimulating reading for musicians, music lovers, and philosophers of the arts. iv + 188pp. 5⅜ x 8½.
T320 Paperbound **$1.45**

Language Books and Records

GERMAN: HOW TO SPEAK AND WRITE IT. AN INFORMAL CONVERSATIONAL METHOD FOR SELF STUDY, Joseph Rosenberg. Eminently useful for self study because of concentration on elementary stages of learning. Also provides teachers with remarkable variety of aids: 28 full- and double-page sketches with pertinent items numbered and identified in German and English; German proverbs, jokes; grammar, idiom studies; extensive practice exercises. The most interesting introduction to German available, full of amusing illustrations, photographs of cities and landmarks in German-speaking cities, cultural information subtly woven into conversational material. Includes summary of grammar, guide to letter writing, study guide to German literature by Dr. Richard Friedenthal. Index. 400 illustrations. 384pp. 5⅜ x 8½.
T271 Paperbound **$2.00**

FRENCH: HOW TO SPEAK AND WRITE IT. AN INFORMAL CONVERSATIONAL METHOD FOR SELF STUDY, Joseph Lemaitre. Even the absolute beginner can acquire a solid foundation for further study from this delightful elementary course. Photographs, sketches and drawings, sparkling colloquial conversations on a wide variety of topics (including French culture and custom), French sayings and quips, are some of aids used to demonstrate rather than merely describe the language. Thorough yet surprisingly entertaining approach, excellent for teaching and for self study. Comprehensive analysis of pronunciation, practice exercises and appendices of verb tables, additional vocabulary, other useful material. Index. Appendix. 400 illustrations. 416pp. 5⅜ x 8½.
T268 Paperbound **$2.00**

DICTIONARY OF SPOKEN SPANISH, Spanish-English, English-Spanish. Compiled from spoken Spanish, emphasizing idiom and colloquial usage in both Castilian and Latin-American. More than 16,000 entries containing over 25,000 idioms—the largest list of idiomatic constructions ever published. Complete sentences given, indexed under single words—language in immediately useable form, for travellers, businessmen, students, etc. 25 page introduction provides rapid survey of sounds, grammar, syntax, with full consideration of irregular verbs. Especially apt in modern treatment of phrases and structure. 17 page glossary gives translations of geographical names, money values, numbers, national holidays, important street signs, useful expressions of high frequency, plus unique 7 page glossary of Spanish and Spanish-American foods and dishes. Originally published as War Department Technical Manual TM 30-900. iv + 513pp. 5⅜ x 8.
T495 Paperbound **$1.75**

SPEAK MY LANGUAGE: SPANISH FOR YOUNG BEGINNERS, M. Ahlman, Z. Gilbert. Records provide one of the best, and most entertaining, methods of introducing a foreign language to children. Within the framework of a train trip from Portugal to Spain, an English-speaking child is introduced to Spanish by a native companion. (Adapted from a successful radio program of the N. Y. State Educational Department.) Though a continuous story, there are·a dozen specific categories of expressions, including greetings, numbers, time, weather, food, clothes, family members, etc. Drill is combined with poetry and contextual use. Authentic background music is heard. An accompanying book enables a reader to follow·the records, and includes a vocabulary of over 350 recorded expressions. Two 10" 33⅓ records, total of 40 minutes. Book. 40 illustrations. 69pp. 5¼ x 10½.
T890 The set **$4.95**

AN ENGLISH-FRENCH-GERMAN-SPANISH WORD FREQUENCY DICTIONARY, H. S. Eaton. An indispensable language study aid, this is a semantic frequency list of the 6000 most frequently used words in 4 languages—24,000 words in all. The lists, based on concepts rather than words alone, and containing all modern, exact, and idiomatic vocabulary, are arranged side by side to form a unique 4-language dictionary. A simple key indicates the importance of the individual words within each language. Over 200 pages of separate indexes for each language enable you to locate individual words at a glance. Will help language teachers and students, authors of textbooks, grammars, and language tests to compare concepts in the various languages and to concentrate on basic vocabulary, avoiding uncommon and obsolete words. 2 Appendixes. xxi + 441pp. 6½ x 9¼.
T738 Paperbound **$2.45**

NEW RUSSIAN-ENGLISH AND ENGLISH-RUSSIAN DICTIONARY, M. A. O'Brien. Over 70,000 entries in the new orthography! Many idiomatic uses and colloquialisms which form the basis of actual speech. Irregular verbs, perfective and imperfective aspects, regular and irregular sound changes, and other features. One of the few dictionaries where accent changes within the conjugation of verbs and the declension of nouns are fully indicated. "One of the best," Prof. E. J. Simmons, Cornell. First names, geographical terms, bibliography, etc. 738pp. 4½ x 6¼.
T208 Paperbound **$2.00**

96 MOST USEFUL PHRASES FOR TOURISTS AND STUDENTS in English, French, Spanish, German, Italian. A handy folder you'll want to carry with you. How to say "Excuse me," "How much is it?", "Write it down, please," etc., in four foreign languages. Copies limited, no more than 1 to a customer.
FREE

Say It language phrase books

These handy phrase books (128 to 196 pages each) make grammatical drills unnecessary for an elementary knowledge of a spoken foreign language. Covering most matters of travel and everyday life each volume contains:

> Over 1000 phrases and sentences in immediately useful forms — foreign language plus English.

> Modern usage designed for Americans. Specific phrases like, "Give me small change," and "Please call a taxi."

> Simplified phonetic transcription you will be able to read at sight.

> The only completely indexed phrase books on the market.

> Covers scores of important situations: — Greetings, restaurants, sightseeing, useful expressions, etc.

These books are prepared by native linguists who are professors at Columbia, N.Y.U., Fordham and other great universities. Use them independently or with any other book or record course. They provide a supplementary living element that most other courses lack. Individual volumes in:

Russian 75¢	Italian 75¢	Spanish 75¢	German 75¢
Hebrew 75¢	Danish 75¢	Japanese 75¢	Swedish 75¢
Dutch 75¢	Esperanto 75¢	Modern Greek 75¢	Portuguese 75¢
Norwegian 75¢	Polish 75¢	French 75¢	Yiddish 75¢
Turkish 75¢		English for German-speaking people 75¢	
English for Italian-speaking people 75¢		English for Spanish-speaking people 75¢	

Large clear type. 128-196 pages each. 3½ x 5¼. Sturdy paper binding.

Listen and Learn language records

LISTEN & LEARN is the only language record course designed especially to meet your travel and everyday needs. It is available in separate sets for FRENCH, SPANISH, GERMAN, JAPANESE, RUSSIAN, MODERN GREEK, PORTUGUESE, ITALIAN and HEBREW, and each set contains three 33⅓ rpm long-playing records—1½ hours of recorded speech by eminent native speakers who are professors at Columbia, New York University, Queens College.

Check the following special features found only in LISTEN & LEARN:

- **Dual-language recording. 812 selected phrases and sentences, over 3200 words,** spoken first in English, then in their foreign language equivalents. A suitable pause follows each foreign phrase, allowing you time to repeat the expression. You learn by unconscious assimilation.

- **128 to 206-page manual** contains everything on the records, plus a simple phonetic pronunciation guide.

- **Indexed for convenience. The only set on the market** that is completely indexed. No more puzzling over where to find the phrase you need. Just look in the rear of the manual.

- **Practical.** No time wasted on material you can find in any grammar. LISTEN & LEARN covers central core material with phrase approach. Ideal for the person with limited learning time.

- **Living, modern expressions,** not found in other courses. Hygienic products, modern equipment, shopping—expressions used every day, like "nylon" and "air-conditioned."

- **Limited objective.** Everything you learn, no matter where you stop, is immediately useful. You have to finish other courses, wade through grammar and vocabulary drill, before they help you.

- **High-fidelity recording.** LISTEN & LEARN records equal in clarity and surface-silence any record on the market costing up to $6.

"Excellent . . . the spoken records . . . impress me as being among the very best on the market," **Prof. Mario Pei,** Dept. of Romance Languages, Columbia University. "Inexpensive and well-done . . . it would make an ideal present," CHICAGO SUNDAY TRIBUNE. "More genuinely helpful than anything of its kind which I have previously encountered," **Sidney Clark,** well-known author of "ALL THE BEST" travel books.

UNCONDITIONAL GUARANTEE. Try LISTEN & LEARN, then return it within 10 days for full refund if you are not satisfied.

Each set contains three twelve-inch 33⅓ records, manual, and album.

SPANISH	the set $5.95	GERMAN	the set $5.95
FRENCH	the set $5.95	ITALIAN	the set $5.95
RUSSIAN	the set $5.95	JAPANESE	the set $5.95
PORTUGUESE	the set $5.95	MODERN GREEK	the set $5.95
MODERN HEBREW	the set $5.95		

Trubner Colloquial Manuals

These unusual books are members of the famous Trubner series of colloquial manuals. They have been written to provide adults with a sound colloquial knowledge of a foreign language, and are suited for either class use or self-study. Each book is a complete course in itself, with progressive, easy to follow lessons. Phonetics, grammar, and syntax are covered, while hundreds of phrases and idioms, reading texts, exercises, and vocabulary are included. These books are unusual in being neither skimpy nor overdetailed in grammatical matters, and in presenting up-to-date, colloquial, and practical phrase material. Bilingual presentation is stressed, to make thorough self-study easier for the reader.

COLLOQUIAL HINDUSTANI, A. H. Harley, formerly Nizam's Reader in Urdu, U. of London. 30 pages on phonetics and scripts (devanagari & Arabic-Persian) are followed by 29 lessons, including material on English and Arabic-Persian influences. Key to all exercises. Vocabulary. 5 x 7½. 147pp.
Clothbound $1.75

COLLOQUIAL PERSIAN, L. P. Elwell-Sutton. Best introduction to modern Persian, with 90 page grammatical section followed by conversations, 35-page vocabulary. 139pp.
Clothbound $1.75

COLLOQUIAL ARABIC, DeLacy O'Leary. Foremost Islamic scholar covers language of Egypt, Syria, Palestine, & Northern Arabia. Extremely clear coverage of complex Arabic verbs & noun plurals; also cultural aspects of language. Vocabulary. xviii + 192pp. 5 x 7½.
Clothbound $2.50

COLLOQUIAL GERMAN, P. F. Doring. Intensive thorough coverage of grammar in easily-followed form. Excellent for brush-up, with hundreds of colloquial phrases. 34 pages of bilingual texts. 224pp. 5 x 7½.
Clothbound $1.75

COLLOQUIAL SPANISH, W. R. Patterson. Castilian grammar and colloquial language, loaded with bilingual phrases and colloquialisms. Excellent for review or self-study. 164pp. 5 x 7½.
Clothbound $1.75

COLLOQUIAL FRENCH, W. R. Patterson. 16th revision of this extremely popular manual. Grammar explained with model clarity, and hundreds of useful expressions and phrases; exercises, reading texts, etc. Appendixes of new and useful words and phrases. 223pp. 5 x 7½.
Clothbound $1.75

COLLOQUIAL CZECH, J. Schwarz, former headmaster of Lingua Institute, Prague. Full easily followed coverage of grammar, hundreds of immediately useable phrases, texts. Perhaps the best Czech grammar in print. "An absolutely successful textbook," JOURNAL OF CZECHO-SLOVAK FORCES IN GREAT BRITAIN. 252pp. 5 x 7½.
Clothbound $3.00

COLLOQUIAL RUMANIAN, G. Nandris, Professor of University of London. Extremely thorough coverage of phonetics, grammar, syntax; also included 70-page reader, and 70-page vocabulary. Probably the best grammar for this increasingly important language. 340pp. 5 x 7½.
Clothbound $2.50

COLLOQUIAL ITALIAN, A. L. Hayward. Excellent self-study course in grammar, vocabulary, idioms, and reading. Easy progressive lessons will give a good working knowledge of Italian in the shortest possible time. 5 x 7½.
Clothbound $1.75

COLLOQUIAL TURKISH, Yusuf Mardin. Very clear, thorough introduction to leading cultural and economic language of Near East. Begins with pronunciation and statement of vowel harmony, then 36 lessons present grammar, graded vocabulary, useful phrases, dialogues, reading, exercises. Key to exercises at rear. Turkish-English vocabulary. All in Roman alphabet. x + 288pp. 4¾ x 7¼.
Clothbound $4.00

DUTCH-ENGLISH AND ENGLISH-DUTCH DICTIONARY, F. G. Renier. For travel, literary, scientific or business Dutch, you will find this the most convenient, practical and comprehensive dictionary on the market. More than 60,000 entries, shades of meaning, colloquialisms, idioms, compounds and technical terms. Dutch and English strong and irregular verbs. This is the only dictionary in its size and price range that indicates the gender of nouns. New orthography. xvii + 571pp. 5½ x 6¼.
T224 Clothbound $2.75

LEARN DUTCH, F. G. Renier. This book is the most satisfactory and most easily used grammar of modern Dutch. The student is gradually led from simple lessons in pronunciation, through translation from and into Dutch, and finally to a mastery of spoken and written Dutch. Grammatical principles are clearly explained while a useful, practical vocabulary is introduced in easy exercises and readings. It is used and recommended by the Fulbright Committee in the Netherlands. Phonetic appendices. Over 1200 exercises; Dutch-English, English-Dutch vocabularies. 181pp. 4¼ x 7¼.
T441 Clothbound $2.25

Literature, History of Literature

ARISTOTLE'S THEORY OF POETRY AND THE FINE ARTS, edited by S. H. Butcher. The celebrated Butcher translation of this great classic faced, page by page, with the complete Greek text. A 300 page introduction discussing Aristotle's ideas and their influence in the history of thought and literature, and covering art and nature, imitation as an aesthetic form, poetic truth, art and morality, tragedy, comedy, and similar topics. Modern Aristotelian criticism discussed by John Gassner. lxxvi + 421pp. 5⅜ x 8.　　　　　　　　　T42 Paperbound **$2.00**

INTRODUCTIONS TO ENGLISH LITERATURE, edited by B. Dobrée. Goes far beyond ordinary histories, ranging from the 7th century up to 1914 (to the 1940's in some cases.) The first half of each volume is a specific detailed study of historical and economic background of the period and a general survey of poetry and prose, including trends of thought, influences, etc. The second and larger half is devoted to a detailed study of more than 5000 poets, novelists, dramatists; also economists, historians, biographers, religious writers, philosophers, travellers, and scientists of literary stature, with dates, lists of major works and their dates, keypoint critical bibliography, and evaluating comments. The most compendious bibliographic and literary aid within its price range.

Vol. I. THE BEGINNINGS OF ENGLISH LITERATURE TO SKELTON, (1509), W. L. Renwick, H. Orton. 450pp. 5⅛ x 7⅞.　　　　　　　　　　　　　　　　　T75 Clothbound **$4.50**

Vol. II. THE ENGLISH RENAISSANCE, 1510-1688, V. de Sola Pinto. 381pp. 5⅛ x 7⅞.
　　　　　　　　　　　　　　　　　　　　　　　　　　　　　T76 Clothbound **$4.50**

Vol. III. AUGUSTANS AND ROMANTICS, 1689-1830, H. Dyson, J. Butt. 320pp. 5⅛ x 7⅞.
　　　　　　　　　　　　　　　　　　　　　　　　　　　　　T77 Clothbound **$4.50**

Vol. IV. THE VICTORIANS AND AFTER, 1830-1940's, E. Batho, B. Dobrée. 360pp. 5⅛ x 7⅞.
　　　　　　　　　　　　　　　　　　　　　　　　　　　　　T78 Clothbound **$4.50**

EPIC AND ROMANCE, W. P. Ker. Written by one of the foremost authorities on medieval literature, this is the standard survey of medieval epic and romance. It covers Teutonic epics, Icelandic sagas, Beowulf, French chansons de geste, the Roman de Troie, and many other important works of literature. It is an excellent account for a body of literature whose beauty and value has only recently come to be recognized. Index. xxiv + 398pp. 5⅜ x 8.
　　　　　　　　　　　　　　　　　　　　　　　　　　　　　T355 Paperbound **$2.00**

THE POPULAR BALLAD, F. B. Gummere. Most useful factual introduction; fund of descriptive material; quotes, cites over 260 ballads. Examines, from folkloristic view, structure; choral, ritual elements; meter, diction, fusion; effects of tradition, editors; almost every other aspect of border, riddle, kinship, sea, ribald, supernatural, etc., ballads. Bibliography. 2 indexes. 374pp. 5⅜ x 8.　　　　　　　　　　　　　　　　　T548 Paperbound **$1.65**

MASTERS OF THE DRAMA, John Gassner. The most comprehensive history of the drama in print, covering drama in every important tradition from the Greeks to the Near East, China, Japan, Medieval Europe, England, Russia, Italy, Spain, Germany, and dozens of other drama producing nations. This unsurpassed reading and reference work encompasses more than 800 dramatists and over 2000 plays, with biographical material, plot summaries, theatre history, etc. "Has no competitors in its field," THEATRE ARTS. "Best of its kind in English," NEW REPUBLIC. Exhaustive 35 page bibliography. 77 photographs and drawings. Deluxe edition with reinforced cloth binding, headbands, stained top. xxii + 890pp. 5⅜ x 8.　　　　T100 Clothbound **$6.95**

THE DEVELOPMENT OF DRAMATIC ART, D. C. Stuart. The basic work on the growth of Western drama from primitive beginnings to Eugene O'Neill, covering over 2500 years. Not a mere listing or survey, but a thorough analysis of changes, origins of style, and influences in each period; dramatic conventions, social pressures, choice of material, plot devices, stock situations, etc.; secular and religious works of all nations and epochs. "Generous and thoroughly documented researches," Outlook. "Solid studies of influences and playwrights and periods," London Times. Index. Bibliography. xi + 679pp. 5⅜ x 8.
　　　　　　　　　　　　　　　　　　　　　　　　　　　　　T693 Paperbound **$2.75**

A SOURCE BOOK IN THEATRICAL HISTORY (SOURCES OF THEATRICAL HISTORY), A. M. Nagler. Over 2000 years of actors, directors, designers, critics, and spectators speak for themselves in this potpourri of writings selected from the great and formative periods of western drama. On-the-spot descriptions of masks, costumes, makeup, rehearsals, special effects, acting methods, backstage squabbles, theatres, etc. Contemporary glimpses of Molière rehearsing his company, an exhortation to a Roman audience to buy refreshments and keep quiet, Goethe's rules for actors, Belasco telling of $6500 he spent building a river, Restoration actors being told to avoid "lewd, obscene, or indecent postures," and much more. Each selection has an introduction by Prof. Nagler. This extraordinary, lively collection is ideal as a source of otherwise difficult to obtain material, as well as a fine book for browsing. Over 80 illustrations. 10 diagrams. xxiii + 611pp. 5⅜ x 8.　　　T515 Paperbound **$2.75**

CATALOGUE OF DOVER BOOKS

WORLD DRAMA, B. H. Clark. The dramatic creativity of a score of ages and eras — all in two handy compact volumes. Over ⅓ of this material is unavailable in any other current edition! 46 plays from Ancient Greece, Rome, Medieval Europe, France, Germany, Italy, England, Russia, Scandinavia, India, China, Japan, etc. — including classic authors like Aeschylus, Sophocles, Euripides, Aristophanes, Plautus, Marlowe, Jonson, Farquhar, Goldsmith, Cervantes, Molière, Dumas, Goethe, Schiller, Ibsen, and many others. This creative collection avoids hackneyed material and includes only completely first-rate works which are relatively little known or difficult to obtain. "The most comprehensive collection of important plays from all literature available in English," SAT. REV. OF LITERATURE. Introduction. Reading lists. 2 volumes. 1364pp. 5⅜ x 8.

Vol. 1, T57 Paperbound **$2.25**
Vol. 2, T59 Paperbound **$2.25**

MASTERPIECES OF THE RUSSIAN DRAMA, edited with introduction by G. R. Noyes. This only comprehensive anthology of Russian drama ever published in English offers complete texts, in 1st-rate modern translations, of 12 plays covering 200 years. Vol. 1: "The Young Hopeful," Fonvisin; "Wit Works Woe," Griboyedov; "The Inspector General," Gogol; "A Month in the Country," Turgenev; "The Poor Bride," Ostrovsky; "A Bitter Fate," Pisemsky. Vol. 2: "The Death of Ivan the Terrible," Alexey Tolstoy "The Power of Darkness," Lev Tolstoy; "The Lower Depths," Gorky; "The Cherry Orchard," Chekhov; "Professor Storitsyn," Andreyev; "Mystery Bouffe," Mayakovsky. Bibliography. Total of 902pp. 5⅜ x 8.

Vol. 1 T647 Paperbound **$2.00**
Vol. 2 T648 Paperbound **$2.00**

EUGENE O'NEILL: THE MAN AND HIS PLAYS, B. H. Clark. Introduction to O'Neill's life and work. Clark analyzes each play from the early THE WEB to the recently produced MOON FOR THE MISBEGOTTEN and THE ICEMAN COMETH revealing the environmental and dramatic influences necessary for a complete understanding of these important works. Bibliography. Appendices. Index. ix + 182pp. 5⅜ x 8.
T379 Paperbound **$1.25**

THE HEART OF THOREAU'S JOURNALS, edited by O. Shepard. The best general selection from Thoreau's voluminous (and rare) journals. This intimate record of thoughts and observations reveals the full Thoreau and his intellectual development more accurately than any of his published works: self-conflict between the scientific observer and the poet, reflections on transcendental philosophy, involvement in the tragedies of neighbors and national causes, etc. New preface, notes, introductions. xii + 228pp. 5⅜ x 8.
T741 Paperbound **$1.45**

H. D. THOREAU: A WRITER'S JOURNAL, edited by L. Stapleton. A unique new selection from the Journals concentrating on Thoreau's growth as a conscious literary artist, the ideals and purposes of his art. Most of the material has never before appeared outside of the complete 14-volume edition. Contains vital insights on Thoreau's projected book on Concord, thoughts on the nature of men and government, indignation with slavery, sources of inspiration, goals in life. Index. xxxiii + 234pp. 5⅜ x 8.
T678 Paperbound **$1.55**

THE HEART OF EMERSON'S JOURNALS, edited by Bliss Perry. Best of these revealing Journals, originally 10 volumes, presented in a one volume edition. Talks with Channing, Hawthorne, Thoreau, and Bronson Alcott; impressions of Webster, Everett, John Brown, and Lincoln; records of moments of sudden understanding, vision, and solitary ecstasy. "The essays do not reveal the power of Emerson's mind . . . as do these hasty and informal writings," N.Y. Times. Preface by Bliss Perry. Index. xiii + 357pp. 5⅜ x 8. T477 Paperbound **$1.85**

FOUNDERS OF THE MIDDLE AGES, E. K. Rand. This is the best non-technical discussion of the transformation of Latin pagan culture into medieval civilization. Covering such figures as Tertullian, Gregory, Jerome, Boethius, Augustine, the Neoplatonists, and many other literary men, educators, classicists, and humanists, this book is a storehouse of information presented clearly and simply for the intelligent non-specialist. "Thoughtful, beautifully written," AMERICAN HISTORICAL REVIEW. "Extraordinarily accurate," Richard McKeon, THE NATION. ix + 365pp. 5⅜ x 8.
T369 Paperbound **$1.85**

PLAY-MAKING: A MANUAL OF CRAFTSMANSHIP, William Archer. With an extensive, new introduction by John Gassner, Yale Univ. The permanently essential requirements of solid play construction are set down in clear, practical language: theme, exposition, foreshadowing, tension, obligatory scene, peripety, dialogue, character, psychology, other topics. This book has been one of the most influential elements in the modern theatre, and almost everything said on the subject since is contained explicitly or implicitly within its covers. Bibliography. Index. xlii + 277pp. 5⅜ x 8.
T651 Paperbound **$1.75**

HAMBURG DRAMATURGY, G. E. Lessing. One of the most brilliant of German playwrights of the eighteenth-century age of criticism analyzes the complex of theory and tradition that constitutes the world of theater. These 104 essays on aesthetic theory helped demolish the regime of French classicism, opening the door to psychological and social realism, romanticism. Subjects include the original functions of tragedy; drama as the rational world; the meaning of pity and fear, pity and fear as means for purgation and other Aristotelian concepts; genius and creative force; interdependence of poet's language and actor's interpretation; truth and authenticity; etc. A basic and enlightening study for anyone interested in aesthetics and ideas, from the philosopher to the theatergoer. Introduction by Prof. Victor Lange. xxii + 265pp. 4½ x 6⅜.
T32 Paperbound **$1.45**

Orientalia

ORIENTAL RELIGIONS IN ROMAN PAGANISM, F. Cumont. A study of the cultural meeting of east and west in the Early Roman Empire. It covers the most important eastern religions of the time from their first appearance in Rome, 204 B.C., when the Great Mother of the Gods was first brought over from Syria. The ecstatic cults of Syria and Phrygia — Cybele, Attis, Adonis, their orgies and mutilatory rites; the mysteries of Egypt — Serapis, Isis, Osiris, the dualism of Persia, the elevation of cosmic evil to equal stature with the deity, Mithra; worship of Hermes Trismegistus; Ishtar, Astarte; the magic of the ancient Near East, etc. Introduction. 55pp. of notes; extensive bibliography. Index. xxiv + 298pp. 5⅜ x 8.
T321 Paperbound **$1.75**

THE MYSTERIES OF MITHRA, F. Cumont. The definitive coverage of a great ideological struggle between the west and the orient in the first centuries of the Christian era. The origin of Mithraism, a Persian mystery religion, and its association with the Roman army is discussed in detail. Then utilizing fragmentary monuments and texts, in one of the greatest feats of scholarly detection, Dr. Cumont reconstructs the mystery teachings and secret doctrines, the hidden organization and cult of Mithra. Mithraic art is discussed, analyzed, and depicted in 70 illustrations. 239pp. 5⅜ x 8.
T323 Paperbound **$1.85**

CHRISTIAN AND ORIENTAL PHILOSOPHY OF ART, A. K. Coomaraswamy. A unique fusion of philosopher, orientalist, art historian, and linguist, the author discusses such matters as: the true function of aesthetics in art, the importance of symbolism, intellectual and philosophic backgrounds, the role of traditional culture in enriching art, common factors in all great art, the nature of medieval art, the nature of folklore, the beauty of mathematics, and similar topics. 2 illustrations. Bibliography. 148pp. 5⅜ x 8.
T378 Paperbound **$1.25**

TRANSFORMATION OF NATURE IN ART, A. K. Coomaraswamy. Unabridged reissue of a basic work upon Asiatic religious art and philosophy of religion. The theory of religious art in Asia and Medieval Europe (exemplified by Meister Eckhart) is analyzed and developed. Detailed consideration is given to Indian medieval aesthetic manuals, symbolic language in philosophy, the origin and use of images in India, and many other fascinating and little known topics. Glossaries of Sanskrit and Chinese terms. Bibliography. 41pp. of notes. 245pp. 5⅜ x 8.
T368 Paperbound **$1.75**

BUDDHIST LOGIC, F.Th. Stcherbatsky. A study of an important part of Buddhism usually ignored by other books on the subject: the Mahayana buddhistic logic of the school of Dignaga and his followers. First vol. devoted to history of Indian logic with Central Asian continuations, detailed exposition of Dignaga system, including theory of knowledge, the sensible world (causation, perception, ultimate reality) and mental world (judgment, inference, logical fallacies, the syllogism), reality of external world, and negation (law of contradiction, universals, dialectic). Vol. II contains translation of Dharmakirti's Nyayabindu with Dharmamottara's commentary. Appendices cover translations of Tibetan treatises on logic, Hindu attacks on Buddhist logic, etc. The basic work, one of the products of the great St. Petersburg school of Indian studies. Written clearly and with an awareness of Western philosophy and logic; meant for the Asian specialist and for the general reader with only a minimum of background. Vol. I, xii + 559pp. Vol. II, viii + 468pp. 5⅜ x 8½.
T955 Vol. I Paperbound **$2.35**
T956 Vol. II Paperbound **$2.35**
The set **$4.70**

THE TEXTS OF TAOISM. The first inexpensive edition of the complete James Legge translations of the Tao Te King and the writings of Chinese mystic Chuang Tse. Also contains several shorter treatises: the T'ai Shang Tractate of Actions and Their Retributions; the King Kang King, or Classic of Purity; the Yin Fu King, or Classic of the Harmony of the Seen and Unseen; the Yu Shu King, or Classic of the Pivot of Jade; and the Hsia Yung King, or Classic of the Directory for a Day. While there are other translations of the Tao Te King, this is the only translation of Chuang Tse and much of other material. Extensive introduction discusses differences between Taoism, Buddhism, Confucianism; authenticity and arrangement of Tao Te King and writings of Chuang Tse; the meaning of the Tao and basic tenets of Taoism; historical accounts of Lao-tse and followers; other pertinent matters. Clarifying notes incorporated into text. Originally published as Volumes 39, 40 of SACRED BOOKS OF THE EAST series, this has long been recognized as an indispensible collection. Sinologists, philosophers, historians of religion will of course be interested and anyone with an elementary course in Oriental religion or philosophy will understand and profit from these writings. Index. Appendix analyzing thought of Chuang Tse. Vol. I, xxiii + 396pp. Vol. II, viii + 340pp. 5⅜ x 8½.
T990 Vol. I Paperbound **$2.00**
T991 Vol. II Paperbound **$2.00**

Philosophy, Religion

GUIDE TO PHILOSOPHY, C. E. M. Joad. A modern classic which examines many crucial problems which man has pondered through the ages: Does free will exist? Is there plan in the universe? How do we know and validate our knowledge? Such opposed solutions as subjective idealism and realism, chance and teleology, vitalism and logical positivism, are evaluated and the contributions of the great philosophers from the Greeks to moderns like Russell, Whitehead, and others, are considered in the context of each problem. "The finest introduction," BOSTON TRANSCRIPT. Index. Classified bibliography. 592pp. 5⅜ x 8.
T297 Paperbound **$2.00**

HISTORY OF ANCIENT PHILOSOPHY, W. Windelband. One of the clearest, most accurate comprehensive surveys of Greek and Roman philosophy. Discusses ancient philosophy in general, intellectual life in Greece in the 7th and 6th centuries B.C., Thales, Anaximander, Anaximenes, Heraclitus, the Eleatics, Empedocles, Anaxagoras, Leucippus, the Pythagoreans, the Sophists, Socrates, Democritus (20 pages), Plato (50 pages), Aristotle (70 pages), the Peripatetics, Stoics, Epicureans, Sceptics, Neo-platonists, Christian Apologists, etc. 2nd German edition translated by H. E. Cushman. xv + 393pp. 5⅜ x 8.
T357 Paperbound **$1.85**

ILLUSTRATIONS OF THE HISTORY OF MEDIEVAL THOUGHT AND LEARNING, R. L. Poole. Basic analysis of the thought and lives of the leading philosophers and ecclesiastics from the 8th to the 14th century—Abailard, Ockham, Wycliffe, Marsiglio of Padua, and many other great thinkers who carried the torch of Western culture and learning through the "Dark Ages": political, religious, and metaphysical views. Long a standard work for scholars and one of the best introductions to medieval thought for beginners. Index. 10 Appendices. xiii + 327pp. 5⅜ x 8.
T674 Paperbound **$1.85**

PHILOSOPHY AND CIVILIZATION IN THE MIDDLE AGES, M. de Wulf. This semi-popular survey covers aspects of medieval intellectual life such as religion, philosophy, science, the arts, etc. It also covers feudalism vs. Catholicism, rise of the universities, mendicant orders, monastic centers, and similar topics. Unabridged. Bibliography. Index. viii + 320pp. 5⅜ x 8.
T284 Paperbound **$1.85**

AN INTRODUCTION TO SCHOLASTIC PHILOSOPHY, Prof. M. de Wulf. Formerly entitled SCHOLASTICISM OLD AND NEW, this volume examines the central scholastic tradition from St. Anselm, Albertus Magnus, Thomas Aquinas, up to Suarez in the 17th century. The relation of scholasticism to ancient and medieval philosophy and science in general is clear and easily followed. The second part of the book considers the modern revival of scholasticism, the Louvain position, relations with Kantianism and Positivism. Unabridged. xvi + 271pp. 5⅜ x 8.
T296 Clothbound **$3.50**
T283 Paperbound **$1.75**

A HISTORY OF MODERN PHILOSOPHY, H. Höffding. An exceptionally clear and detailed coverage of western philosophy from the Renaissance to the end of the 19th century. Major and minor men such as Pomponazzi, Bodin, Boehme, Telesius, Bruno, Copernicus, da Vinci, Kepler, Galileo, Bacon, Descartes, Hobbes, Spinoza, Leibniz, Wolff, Locke, Newton, Berkeley, Hume, Erasmus, Montesquieu, Voltaire, Diderot, Rousseau, Lessing, Kant, Herder, Fichte, Schelling, Hegel, Schopenhauer, Comte, Mill, Darwin, Spencer, Hartmann, Lange, and many others, are discussed in terms of theory of knowledge, logic, cosmology, and psychology. Index. 2 volumes, total of 1159pp. 5⅜ x 8.
T117 Vol. 1, Paperbound **$2.00**
T118 Vol. 2, Paperbound **$2.00**

ARISTOTLE, A. E. Taylor. A brilliant, searching non-technical account of Aristotle and his thought written by a foremost Platonist. It covers the life and works of Aristotle; classification of the sciences; logic; first philosophy; matter and form; causes; motion and eternity; God; physics; metaphysics; and similar topics. Bibliography. New Index compiled for this edition. 128pp. 5⅜ x 8.
T280 Paperbound **$1.00**

THE SYSTEM OF THOMAS AQUINAS, M. de Wulf. Leading Neo-Thomist, one of founders of University of Louvain, gives concise exposition to central doctrines of Aquinas, as a means toward determining his value to modern philosophy, religion. Formerly "Medieval Philosophy Illustrated from the System of Thomas Aquinas." Trans. by E. Messenger. Introduction. 151pp. 5⅜ x 8.
T568 Paperbound **$1.25**

LEIBNIZ, H. W. Carr. Most stimulating middle-level coverage of basic philosophical thought of Leibniz. Easily understood discussion, analysis of major works: "Theodicy," "Principles of Nature and Grace," "Monadology"; Leibniz's influence; intellectual growth; correspondence; disputes with Bayle, Malebranche, Newton; importance of his thought today, with reinterpretation in modern terminology. "Power and mastery," London Times. Bibliography. Index. 226pp. 5⅜ x 8.
T624 Paperbound **$1.35**

CATALOGUE OF DOVER BOOKS

AN ESSAY CONCERNING HUMAN UNDERSTANDING, John Locke. Edited by A. C. Fraser. Unabridged reprinting of definitive edition; only complete edition of "Essay" in print. Marginal analyses of almost every paragraph; hundreds of footnotes; authoritative 140-page biographical, critical, historical prolegomena. Indexes. 1170pp. 5⅜ x 8.
T530 Vol. 1 (Books 1, 2) Paperbound **$2.25**
T531 Vol. 2 (Books 3, 4) Paperbound **$2.25**
2 volume set **$4.50**

THE PHILOSOPHY OF HISTORY, G. W. F. Hegel. One of the great classics of western thought which reveals Hegel's basic principle: that history is not chance but a rational process, the realization of the Spirit of Freedom. Ranges from the oriental cultures of subjective thought to the classical subjective cultures, to the modern absolute synthesis where spiritual and secular may be reconciled. Translation and introduction by J. Sibree. Introduction by C. Hegel. Special introduction for this edition by Prof. Carl Friedrich. xxxix + 447pp. 5⅜ x 8.
T112 Paperbound **$2.00**

THE PHILOSOPHY OF HEGEL, W. T. Stace. The first detailed analysis of Hegel's thought in English, this is especially valuable since so many of Hegel's works are out of print. Dr. Stace examines Hegel's debt to Greek idealists and the 18th century and then proceeds to a careful description and analysis of Hegel's first principles, categories, reason, dialectic method, his logic, philosophy of nature and spirit, etc. Index. Special 14 x 20 chart of Hegelian system. x + 526pp. 5⅜ x 8.
T254 Paperbound **$2.25**

THE WILL TO BELIEVE and HUMAN IMMORTALITY, W. James. Two complete books bound as one. THE WILL TO BELIEVE discusses the interrelations of belief, will, and intellect in man; chance vs. determinism, free will vs. determinism, free will vs. fate, pluralism vs. monism; the philosophies of Hegel and Spencer, and more. HUMAN IMMORTALITY examines the question of survival after death and develops an unusual and powerful argument for immortality. Two prefaces. Index. Total of 429pp. 5⅜ x 8.
T291 Paperbound **$2.45**

THE WORLD AND THE INDIVIDUAL, Josiah Royce. Only major effort by an American philosopher to interpret nature of things in systematic, comprehensive manner. Royce's formulation of an absolute voluntarism remains one of the original and profound solutions to the problems involved. Part One, Four Historical Conceptions of Being, inquires into first principles, true meaning and place of individuality. Part Two, Nature, Man, and the Moral Order, is application of first principles to problems concerning religion, evil, moral order. Introduction by J. E. Smith, Yale Univ. Index. 1070pp. 5⅜ x 8.
T561 Vol. 1 Paperbound **$2.75**
T562 Vol. 2 Paperbound **$2.75**
Two volume set **$5.50**

THE PHILOSOPHICAL WRITINGS OF PEIRCE, edited by J. Buchler. This book (formerly THE PHILOSOPHY OF PEIRCE) is a carefully integrated exposition of Peirce's complete system composed of selections from his own work. Symbolic logic, scientific method, theory of signs, pragmatism, epistemology, chance, cosmology, ethics, and many other topics are treated by one of the greatest philosophers of modern times. This is the only inexpensive compilation of his key ideas. xvi + 386pp. 5⅜ x 8.
T217 Paperbound **$2.00**

EXPERIENCE AND NATURE, John Dewey. An enlarged, revised edition of the Paul Carus lectures which Dewey delivered in 1925. It covers Dewey's basic formulation of the problem of knowledge, with a full discussion of other systems, and a detailing of his own concepts of the relationship of external world, mind, and knowledge. Starts with a thorough examination of the philosophical method; examines the interrelationship of experience and nature; analyzes experience on basis of empirical naturalism, the formulation of law, role of language and social factors in knowledge; etc. Dewey's treatment of central problems in philosophy is profound but extremely easy to follow. ix + 448pp. 5⅜ x 8.
T471 Paperbound **$2.00**

THE PHILOSOPHICAL WORKS OF DESCARTES. The definitive English edition of all the major philosophical works and letters of René Descartes. All of his revolutionary insights, from his famous "Cogito ergo sum" to his detailed account of contemporary science and his astonishingly fruitful concept that all phenomena of the universe (except mind) could be reduced to clear laws by the use of mathematics. An excellent source for the thought of men like Hobbes, Arnauld, Gassendi, etc., who were Descarte's contemporaries. Translated by E. S. Haldane and G. Ross. Introductory notes. Index. Total of 842pp. 5⅜ x 8.
T71 Vol. 1, Paperbound **$2.00**
T72 Vol. 2, Paperbound **$2.00**

THE CHIEF WORKS OF SPINOZA. An unabridged reprint of the famous Bohn edition containing all of Spinoza's most important works: Vol. I: The Theologico-Political Treatise and the Political Treatise. Vol. II: On The Improvement Of Understanding, The Ethics, Selected Letters. Profound and enduring ideas on God, the universe, pantheism, society, religion, the state, democracy, the mind, emotions, freedom and the nature of man, which influenced Goethe, Hegel, Schelling, Coleridge, Whitehead, and many others. Introduction. 2 volumes. 826pp. 5⅜ x 8.
T249 Vol. I, Paperbound **$1.50**
T250 Vol. II, Paperbound **$1.50**

CATALOGUE OF DOVER BOOKS

THE SENSE OF BEAUTY, G. Santayana. A revelation of the beauty of language as well as an important philosophic treatise, this work studies the "why, when, and how beauty appears, what conditions an object must fulfill to be beautiful, what elements of our nature make us sensible of beauty, and what the relation is between the constitution of the object and the excitement of our susceptibility." "It is doubtful if a better treatment of the subject has since been published," PEABODY JOURNAL. Index. ix + 275pp. 5⅜ x 8.
T238 Paperbound **$1.00**

PROBLEMS OF ETHICS, Moritz Schlick. The renowned leader of the "Vienna Circle" applies the logical positivist approach to a wide variety of ethical problems: the source and means of attaining knowledge, the formal and material characteristics of the good, moral norms and principles, absolute vs. relative values, free will and responsibility, comparative importance of pleasure and suffering as ethical values, etc. Disarmingly simple and straightforward despite complexity of subject. First English translation, authorized by author before his death, of a thirty-year old classic. Translated and with an introduction by David Rynin. Index. Foreword by Prof. George P. Adams. xxi + 209pp. 5⅜ x 8.
T946 Paperbound **$1.45**

AN INTRODUCTION TO EXISTENTIALISM, Robert G. Olson. A new and indispensable guide to one of the major thought systems of our century, the movement that is central to the thinking of some of the most creative figures of the past hundred years. Stresses Heidegger and Sartre, with careful and objective examination of the existentialist position, values—freedom of choice, individual dignity, personal love, creative effort—and answers to the eternal questions of the human condition. Scholarly, unbiased, analytic, unlike most studies of this difficult subject, Prof. Olson's book is aimed at the student of philosophy as well as at the reader with no formal training who is looking for an absorbing, accessible, and thorough introduction to the basic texts. Index. xv + 221pp. 5⅜ x 8½.
T55 Paperbound **$1.45**

SYMBOLIC LOGIC, C. I. Lewis and C. H. Langford. Since first publication in 1932, this has been among most frequently cited works on symbolic logic. Still one of the best introductions both for beginners and for mathematicians, philosophers. First part covers basic topics which easily lend themselves to beginning study. Second part is rigorous, thorough development of logistic method, examination of some of most difficult and abstract aspects of symbolic logic, including modal logic, logical paradoxes, many-valued logic, with Prof. Lewis' own contributions. 2nd revised (corrected) edition. 3 appendixes, one new to this edition. 524pp. 5⅜ x 8.
S170 Paperbound **$2.00**

WHITEHEAD'S PHILOSOPHY OF CIVILIZATION, A. H. Johnson. A leading authority on Alfred North Whitehead synthesizes the great philosopher's thought on civilization, scattered throughout various writings, into unified whole. Analysis of Whitehead's general definition of civilization, his reflections on history and influences on its development, his religion, including his analysis of Christianity, concept of solitariness as first requirement of personal religion, and so on. Other chapters cover views on minority groups, society, civil liberties, education. Also critical comments on Whitehead's philosophy. Written with general reader in mind. A perceptive introduction to important area of the thought of a leading philosopher of our century. Revised index and bibliography. xii + 211pp. 5⅜ x 8½.
T996 Paperbound **$1.50**

WHITEHEAD'S THEORY OF REALITY, A. H. Johnson. Introductory outline of Whitehead's theory of actual entities, the heart of his philosophy of reality, followed by his views on nature of God, philosophy of mind, theory of value (truth, beauty, goodness and their opposites), analyses of other philosophers, attitude toward science. A perspicacious lucid introduction by author of dissertation on Whitehead, written under the subject's supervision at Harvard. Good basic view for beginning students of philosophy and for those who are simply interested in important contemporary ideas. Revised index and bibliography. xiii + 267pp. 5⅜ x 8½.
T989 Paperbound **$1.50**

MIND AND THE WORLD-ORDER, C. I. Lewis. Building upon the work of Peirce, James, and Dewey, Professor Lewis outlines a theory of knowledge in terms of "conceptual pragmatism." Dividing truth into abstract mathematical certainty and empirical truth, the author demonstrates that the traditional understanding of the a priori must be abandoned. Detailed analyses of philosophy, metaphysics, method, the "given" in experience, knowledge of objects, nature of the a priori, experience and order, and many others. Appendices. xiv + 446pp. 5⅜ x 8.
T359 Paperbound **$2.25**

SCEPTICISM AND ANIMAL FAITH, G. Santayana. To eliminate difficulties in the traditional theory of knowledge, Santayana distinguishes between the independent existence of objects and the essence our mind attributes to them. Scepticism is thereby established as a form of belief, and animal faith is shown to be a necessary condition of knowledge. Belief, classical idealism, intuition, memory, symbols, literary psychology, and much more, discussed with unusual clarity and depth. Index. xii + 314pp. 5⅜ x 8.
T235 Clothbound **$3.50**
T236 Paperbound **$1.50**

LANGUAGE AND MYTH, E. Cassirer. Analyzing the non-rational thought processes which go to make up culture, Cassirer demonstrates that beneath both language and myth there lies a dominant unconscious "grammar" of experience whose categories and canons are not those of logical thought. His analyses of seemingly diverse phenomena such as Indian metaphysics, the Melanesian "mana," the Naturphilosophie of Schelling, modern poetry, etc., are profound without being pedantic. Introduction and translation by Susanne Langer. Index. x + 103pp. 5⅜ x 8.
T51 Paperbound **$1.25**

THE ANALYSIS OF MATTER, Bertrand Russell. A classic which has retained its importance in understanding the relation between modern physical theory and human perception. Logical analysis of physics, prerelativity physics, causality, scientific inference, Weyl's theory, tensors, invariants and physical interpretations, periodicity, and much more is treated with Russell's usual brilliance. "Masterly piece of clear thinking and clear writing," NATION AND ATHENAEUM. "Most thorough treatment of the subject," THE NATION. Introduction. Index. 8 figures. viii + 408pp. 5⅜ x 8.   S231 Paperbound **$1.95**

CONCEPTUAL THINKING (A LOGICAL INQUIRY), S. Körner. Discusses origin, use of general concepts on which language is based, and the light they shed on basic philosophical questions. Rigorously examines how different concepts are related; how they are linked to experience; problems in the field of contact between exact logical, mathematical, and scientific concepts, and the inexactness of everyday experience (studied at length). This work elaborates many new approaches to the traditional problems of philosophy—epistemology, value theories, metaphysics, aesthetics, morality. "Rare originality . . . brings a new rigour into philosophical argument," Philosophical Quarterly. New corrected second edition. Index. vii + 301pp. 5⅜ x 8   T516 Paperbound **$1.75**

INTRODUCTION TO SYMBOLIC LOGIC, S. Langer. No special knowledge of math required — probably the clearest book ever written on symbolic logic, suitable for the layman, general scientist, and philosopher. You start with simple symbols and advance to a knowledge of the Boole-Schroeder and Russell-Whitehead systems. Forms, logical structure, classes, the calculus of propositions, logic of the syllogism, etc., are all covered. "One of the clearest and simplest introductions," MATHEMATICS GAZETTE. Second enlarged, revised edition. 368pp. 5⅜ x 8.   S164 Paperbound **$1.75**

LANGUAGE, TRUTH AND LOGIC, A. J. Ayer. A clear, careful analysis of the basic ideas of Logical Positivism. Building on the work of Schlick, Russell, Carnap, and the Viennese School, Mr. Ayer develops a detailed exposition of the nature of philosophy, science, and metaphysics; the Self and the World; logic and common sense, and other philosophic concepts. An aid to clarity of thought as well as the first full-length development of Logical Positivism in English. Introduction by Bertrand Russell. Index. 160pp. 5⅜ x 8.   T10 Paperbound **$1.25**

ESSAYS IN EXPERIMENTAL LOGIC, J. Dewey. Based upon the theory that knowledge implies a judgment which in turn implies an inquiry, these papers consider the inquiry stage in terms of: the relationship of thought and subject matter, antecedents of thought, data and meanings. 3 papers examine Bertrand Russell's thought, while 2 others discuss pragmatism and a final essay presents a new theory of the logic of values. Index. viii + 444pp. 5⅜ x 8.
                                                                 T73 Paperbound **$1.95**

TRAGIC SENSE OF LIFE, M. de Unamuno. The acknowledged masterpiece of one of Spain's most influential thinkers. Between the despair at the inevitable death of man and all his works and the desire for something better, Unamuno finds that "saving incertitude" that alone can console us. This dynamic appraisal of man's faith in God and in himself has been called "a masterpiece" by the ENCYCLOPAEDIA BRITANNICA. xxx + 332pp. 5⅜ x 8.
                                                                 T257 Paperbound **$2.00**

HISTORY OF DOGMA, A. Harnack. Adolph Harnack, who died in 1930, was perhaps the greatest Church historian of all time. In this epoch-making history, which has never been surpassed in comprehensiveness and wealth of learning, he traces the development of the authoritative Christian doctrinal system from its first crystallization in the 4th century down through the Reformation, including also a brief survey of the later developments through the Infallibility decree of 1870. He reveals the enormous influence of Greek thought on the early Fathers, and discusses such topics as the Apologists, the great councils, Manichaeism, the historical position of Augustine, the medieval opposition to indulgences, the rise of Protestantism, the relations of Luther's doctrines with modern tendencies of thought, and much more. "Monumental work; still the most valuable history of dogma . . . luminous analysis of the problems . . . abounds in suggestion and stimulus and can be neglected by no one who desires to understand the history of thought in this most important field," Dutcher's Guide to Historical Literature. Translated by Neil Buchanan. Index. Unabridged reprint in 4 volumes. Vol I: Beginnings to the Gnostics and Marcion. Vol II & III: 2nd century to the 4th century Fathers. Vol IV & V: 4th century Councils to the Carlovingian Renaissance. Vol VI & VII: Period of Clugny (c. 1000) to the Reformation, and after. Total of cii + 2407pp. 5⅜ x 8.
                                 T904 Vol I   Paperbound **$2.50**
                                 T905 Vol II & III   Paperbound **$2.50**
                                 T906 Vol IV & V   Paperbound **$2.50**
                                 T907 Vol VI & VII   Paperbound **$2.50**
                                                     The set **$10.00**

THE GUIDE FOR THE PERPLEXED, Maimonides. One of the great philosophical works of all time and a necessity for everyone interested in the philosophy of the Middle Ages in the Jewish, Christian, and Moslem traditions. Maimonides develops a common meeting-point for the Old Testament and the Aristotelian thought which pervaded the medieval world. His ideas and methods predate such scholastics as Aquinas and Scotus and throw light on the entire problem of philosophy or science vs. religion. 2nd revised edition. Complete unabridged Friedländer translation. 55 page introduction to Maimonides's life, period, etc., with an important summary of the GUIDE. Index. lix + 414pp. 5⅜ x 8.   T351 Paperbound **$2.00**

Americana

THE EYES OF DISCOVERY, J. Bakeless. A vivid reconstruction of how unspoiled America appeared to the first white men. Authentic and enlightening accounts of Hudson's landing in New York, Coronado's trek through the Southwest; scores of explorers, settlers, trappers, soldiers. America's pristine flora, fauna, and Indians in every region and state in fresh and unusual new aspects. "A fascinating view of what the land was like before the first highway went through," Time. 68 contemporary illustrations, 39 newly added in this edition. Index. Bibliography. x + 500pp. 5⅜ x 8.   T761 Paperbound **$2.00**

AUDUBON AND HIS JOURNALS, J. J. Audubon. A collection of fascinating accounts of Europe and America in the early 1800's through Audubon's own eyes. Includes the Missouri River Journals —an eventful trip through America's untouched heartland, the Labrador Journals, the European Journals, the famous "Episodes", and other rare Audubon material, including the descriptive chapters from the original letterpress edition of the "Ornithological Studies", omitted in all later editions. Indispensable for ornithologists, naturalists, and all lovers of Americana and adventure. 70-page biography by Audubon's granddaughter. 38 illustrations. Index. Total of 1106pp. 5⅜ x 8.   T675 Vol I Paperbound **$2.25**
                                                   T676 Vol II Paperbound **$2.25**
                                                   The set **$4.50**

TRAVELS OF WILLIAM BARTRAM, edited by Mark Van Doren. The first inexpensive illustrated edition of one of the 18th century's most delightful books is an excellent source of first-hand material on American geography, anthropology, and natural history. Many descriptions of early Indian tribes are our only source of information on them prior to the infiltration of the white man. "The mind of a scientist with the soul of a poet," John Livingston Lowes. 13 original illustrations and maps. Edited with an introduction by Mark Van Doren. 448pp. 5⅜ x 8.
                                                   T13 Paperbound **$2.00**

GARRETS AND PRETENDERS: A HISTORY OF BOHEMIANISM IN AMERICA, A. Parry. The colorful and fantastic history of American Bohemianism from Poe to Kerouac. This is the only complete record of hoboes, cranks, starving poets, and suicides. Here are Pfaff, Whitman, Crane, Bierce, Pound, and many others. New chapters by the author and by H. T. Moore bring this thorough and well-documented history down to the Beatniks. "An excellent account," N. Y. Times. Scores of cartoons, drawings, and caricatures. Bibliography. Index. xxviii + 421pp. 5⅝ x 8⅜.   T708 Paperbound **$1.95**

THE EXPLORATION OF THE COLORADO RIVER AND ITS CANYONS, J. W. Powell. The thrilling first-hand account of the expedition that filled in the last white space on the map of the United States. Rapids, famine, hostile Indians, and mutiny are among the perils encountered as the unknown Colorado Valley reveals its secrets. This is the only uncut version of Major Powell's classic of exploration that has been printed in the last 60 years. Includes later reflections and subsequent expedition. 250 illustrations, new map. 400pp. 5⅝ x 8⅜.
                                                   T94 Paperbound **$2.00**

THE JOURNAL OF HENRY D. THOREAU, Edited by Bradford Torrey and Francis H. Allen. Henry Thoreau is not only one of the most important figures in American literature and social thought; his voluminous journals (from which his books emerged as selections and crystalliza-tions) constitute both the longest, most sensitive record of personal internal development and a most penetrating description of a historical moment in American culture. This present set, which was first issued in fourteen volumes, contains Thoreau's entire journals from 1837 to 1862, with the exception of the lost years which were found only recently. We are reissuing it, complete and unabridged, with a new introduction by Walter Harding, Secretary of the Thoreau Society. Fourteen volumes reissued in two volumes. Foreword by Henry Seidel Canby. Total of 1888pp. 8⅜ x 12¼.   T312-3 Two volume set, Clothbound **$20.00**

GAMES AND SONGS OF AMERICAN CHILDREN, collected by William Wells Newell. A remarkable collection of 190 games with songs that accompany many of them; cross references to show similarities, differences among them; variations; musical notation for 38 songs. Textual dis-cussions show relations with folk-drama and other aspects of folk tradition. Grouped into categories for ready comparative study: Love-games, histories, playing at work, human life, bird and beast, mythology, guessing-games, etc. New introduction covers relations of songs and dances to timeless heritage of folklore, biographical sketch of Newell, other pertinent data. A good source of inspiration for those in charge of groups of children and a valuable reference for anthropologists, sociologists, psychiatrists. Introduction by Carl Withers. New indexes of first lines, games. 5⅜ x 8½. xii + 242pp.   T354 Paperbound **$1.65**

CATALOGUE OF DOVER BOOKS

GARDNER'S PHOTOGRAPHIC SKETCH BOOK OF THE CIVIL WAR, Alexander Gardner. The first published collection of Civil War photographs, by one of the two or three most famous photographers of the era, outstandingly reproduced from the original positives. Scenes of crucial battles: Appomattox, Manassas, Mechanicsville, Bull Run, Yorktown, Fredericksburg, etc. Gettysburg immediately after retirement of forces. Battle ruins at Richmond, Petersburg, Gaines'Mill. Prisons, arsenals, a slave pen, fortifications, headquarters, pontoon bridges, soldiers, a field hospital. A unique glimpse into the realities of one of the bloodiest wars in history, with an introductory text to each picture by Gardner himself. Until this edition, there were only five known copies in libraries, and fewer in private hands, one of which sold at auction in 1952 for $425. Introduction by E. F. Bleiler. 100 full page 7 x 10 photographs (original size). 224pp. 8½ x 10¾. T476 Clothbound **$6.00**

A BIBLIOGRAPHY OF NORTH AMERICAN FOLKLORE AND FOLKSONG, Charles Haywood, Ph.D. The only book that brings together bibliographic information on so wide a range of folklore material. Lists practically everything published about American folksongs, ballads, dances, folk beliefs and practices, popular music, tales, similar material—more than 35,000 titles of books, articles, periodicals, monographs, music publications, phonograph records. Each entry complete with author, title, date and place of publication, arranger and performer of particular examples of folk music, many with Dr. Haywood's valuable criticism, evaluation. Volume I, "The American People," is complete listing of general and regional studies, titles of tales and songs of Negro and non-English speaking groups and where to find them, Occupational Bibliography including sections listing sources of information, folk material on cowboys, riverboat men, 49ers, American characters like Mike Fink, Frankie and Johnnie, John Henry, many more. Volume II, "The American Indian," tells where to find information on dances, myths, songs, ritual of more than 250 tribes in U.S., Canada. A monumental product of 10 years' labor, carefully classified for easy use. "All students of this subject . . . will find themselves in debt to Professor Haywood," Stith Thompson, in American Anthropologist. ". . . a most useful and excellent work," Duncan Emrich, Chief Folklore Section, Library of Congress, in "Notes." Corrected, enlarged republication of 1951 edition. New Preface. New index of composers, arrangers, performers. General index of more than 15,000 items. Two volumes. Total of 1301pp. 6⅛ x 9¼. T797-798 Clothbound **$12.50**

INCIDENTS OF TRAVEL IN YUCATAN, John L. Stephens. One of first white men to penetrate interior of Yucatan tells the thrilling story of his discoveries of 44 cities, remains of once-powerful Maya civilization. Compelling text combines narrative power with historical significance as it takes you through heat, dust, storms of Yucatan; native festivals with brutal bull fights; great ruined temples atop man-made mounds. Countless idols, sculptures, tombs, examples of Mayan taste for rich ornamentation, from gateways to personal trinkets, accurately illustrated, discussed in text. Will appeal to those interested in ancient civilizations, and those who like stories of exploration, discovery, adventure. Republication of last (1843) edition. 124 illustrations by English artist, F. Catherwood. Appendix on Mayan architecture, chronology. Two volume set. Total of xxviii + 927pp.
Vol I T926 Paperbound **$2.00**
Vol II T927 Paperbound **$2.00**
The set **$4.00**

A GENIUS IN THE FAMILY, Hiram Percy Maxim. Sir Hiram Stevens Maxim was known to the public as the inventive genius who created the Maxim gun, automatic sprinkler, and a heavier-than-air plane that got off the ground in 1894. Here, his son reminisces—this is by no means a formal biography—about the exciting and often downright scandalous private life of his brilliant, eccentric father. A warm and winning portrait of a prankish, mischievous, impious personality, a genuine character. The style is fresh and direct, the effect is unadulterated pleasure. "A book of charm and lasting humor . . . belongs on the 'must read' list of all fathers," New York Times. "A truly gorgeous affair," New Statesman and Nation. 17 illustrations, 16 specially for this edition. viii + 108pp. 5⅜ x 8½.
T948 Paperbound **$1.00**

HORSELESS CARRIAGE DAYS, Hiram P. Maxim. The best account of an important technological revolution by one of its leading figures. The delightful and rewarding story of the author's experiments with the exact combustibility of gasoline, stopping and starting mechanisms, carriage design, and engines. Captures remarkably well the flavor of an age of scoffers and rival inventors not above sabotage; of noisy, uncontrollable gasoline vehicles and incredible mobile steam kettles. ". . . historic information and light humor are combined to furnish highly entertaining reading," New York Times. 56 photographs, 12 specially for this edition. xi + 175pp. 5⅜ x 8½. T964 Paperbound **$1.35**

BODY, BOOTS AND BRITCHES: FOLKTALES, BALLADS AND SPEECH FROM COUNTRY NEW YORK, Harold W. Thompson. A unique collection, discussion of songs, stories, anecdotes, proverbs handed down orally from Scotch-Irish grandfathers, German nurse-maids, Negro workmen, gathered from all over Upper New York State. Tall tales by and about lumbermen and pirates, canalers and injun-fighters, tragic and comic ballads, scores of sayings and proverbs all tied together by an informative, delightful narrative by former president of New York Historical Society. ". . . a sparkling homespun tapestry that every lover of Americana will want to have around the house," Carl Carmer, New York Times. Republication of 1939 edition. 20 line-drawings. Index. Appendix (Sources of material, bibliography). 530pp. 5⅜ x 8½. T411 Paperbound **$2.00**

Art, History of Art, Antiques, Graphic Arts, Handcrafts

ART STUDENTS' ANATOMY, E. J. Farris. Outstanding art anatomy that uses chiefly living objects for its illustrations. 71 photos of undraped men, women, children are accompanied by carefully labeled matching sketches to illustrate the skeletal system, articulations and movements, bony landmarks, the muscular system, skin, fasciae, fat, etc. 9 x-ray photos show movement of joints. Undraped models are shown in such actions as serving in tennis, drawing a bow in archery, playing football, dancing, preparing to spring and to dive. Also discussed and illustrated are proportions, age and sex differences, the anatomy of the smile, etc. 8 plates by the great early 18th century anatomic illustrator Siegfried Albinus are also included. Glossary. 158 figures, 7 in color. x + 159pp. 5⅝ x 8⅜. T744 Paperbound **$1.50**

AN ATLAS OF ANATOMY FOR ARTISTS, F Schider. A new 3rd edition of this standard text enlarged by 52 new illustrations of hands, anatomical studies by Cloquet, and expressive life studies of the body by Barcsay. 189 clear, detailed plates offer you precise information of impeccable accuracy. 29 plates show all aspects of the skeleton, with closeups of special areas, while 54 full-page plates, mostly in two colors, give human musculature as seen from four different points of view, with cutaways for important portions of the body. 14 full-page plates provide photographs of hand forms, eyelids, female breasts, and indicate the location of muscles upon models. 59 additional plates show how great artists of the past utilized human anatomy. They reproduce sketches and finished work by such artists as Michelangelo, Leonardo da Vinci, Goya, and 15 others. This is a lifetime reference work which will be one of the most important books in any artist's library. "The standard reference tool," AMERICAN LIBRARY ASSOCIATION. "Excellent," AMERICAN ARTIST. Third enlarged edition. 189 plates, 647 illustrations. xxvi + 192pp. 7⅞ x 10⅝. T241 Clothbound **$6.00**

AN ATLAS OF ANIMAL ANATOMY FOR ARTISTS, W. Ellenberger, H. Baum, H. Dittrich. The largest, richest animal anatomy for artists available in English. 99 detailed anatomical plates of such animals as the horse, dog, cat, lion, deer, seal, kangaroo, flying squirrel, cow, bull, goat, monkey, hare, and bat. Surface features are clearly indicated, while progressive beneath-the-skin pictures show musculature, tendons, and bone structure. Rest and action are exhibited in terms of musculature and skeletal structure and detailed cross-sections are given for heads and important features. The animals chosen are representative of specific families so that a study of these anatomies will provide knowledge of hundreds of related species. "Highly recommended as one of the very few books on the subject worthy of being used as an authoritative guide," DESIGN. "Gives a fundamental knowledge," AMERICAN ARTIST. Second revised, enlarged edition with new plates from Cuvier, Stubbs, etc. 288 illustrations. 153pp. 11⅜ x 9. T82 Clothbound **$6.00**

THE HUMAN FIGURE IN MOTION, Eadweard Muybridge. The largest selection in print of Muybridge's famous high-speed action photos of the human figure in motion. 4789 photographs illustrate 162 different actions: men, women, children—mostly undraped—are shown walking, running, carrying various objects, sitting, lying down, climbing, throwing, arising, and performing over 150 other actions. Some actions are shown in as many as 150 photographs each. All in all there are more than 500 action strips in this enormous volume, series shots taken at shutter speeds of as high as 1/6000th of a second! These are not posed shots, but true stopped motion. They show bone and muscle in situations that the human eye is not fast enough to capture. Earlier, smaller editions of these prints have brought $40 and more on the out-of-print market. "A must for artists," ART IN FOCUS. "An unparalleled dictionary of action for all artists," AMERICAN ARTIST. 390 full-page plates, with 4789 photographs. Printed on heavy glossy stock. Reinforced binding with headbands. xxi + 390pp. 7⅞ x 10⅝. T204 Clothbound **$10.00**

ANIMALS IN MOTION, Eadweard Muybridge. This is the largest collection of animal action photos in print. 34 different animals (horses, mules, oxen, goats, camels, pigs, cats, guanacos, lions, gnus, deer, monkeys, eagles—and 21 others) in 132 characteristic actions. The horse alone is shown in more than 40 different actions. All 3919 photographs are taken in series at speeds up to 1/6000th of a second. The secrets of leg motion, spinal patterns, head movements, strains and contortions shown nowhere else are captured. You will see exactly how a lion sets his foot down; how an elephant's knees are like a human's—and how they differ; the position of a kangaroo's legs in mid-leap; how an ostrich's head bobs; details of the flight of birds—and thousands of facets of motion only the fastest cameras can catch. Photographed from domestic animals and animals in the Philadelphia zoo, it contains neither semiposed artificial shots nor distorted telephoto shots taken under adverse conditions. Artists, biologists, decorators, cartoonists, will find this book indispensable for understanding animals in motion. "A really marvelous series of plates," NATURE (London). "The dry plate's most spectacular early use was by Eadweard Muybridge," LIFE. 3919 photographs; 380 full pages of plates. 440pp. Printed on heavy glossy paper. Deluxe binding with headbands. 7⅞ x 10⅝. T203 Clothbound **$10.00**

THE HISTORY AND TECHNIQUE OF LETTERING, A. Nesbitt. The only thorough inexpensive history of letter forms from the point of view of the artist. Mr. Nesbitt covers every major development in lettering from the ancient Egyptians to the present and illustrates each development with a complete alphabet. Such masters as Baskerville, Bell, Bodoni, Caslon, Koch, Kilian, Morris, Garamont, Jenson, and dozens of others are analyzed in terms of artistry and historical development. The author also presents a 65-page practical course in lettering, besides the full historical text. 89 complete alphabets; 165 additional lettered specimens. xvii + 300pp. 5⅜ x 8. T427 Paperbound **$2.00**

FOOT-HIGH LETTERS: A GUIDE TO LETTERING (A PRACTICAL SYLLABUS FOR TEACHERS), M. Price. A complete alphabet of Classic Roman letters, each a foot high, each on a separate 16 x 22 plate—perfect for use in lettering classes. In addition to an accompanying description, each plate also contains 9 two-inch-high forms of letter in various type faces, such as "Caslon," "Empire," "Onyx," and "Neuland," illustrating the many possible derivations from the standard classical forms. One plate contains 21 additional forms of the letter A. The fully illustrated 16-page syllabus by Mr. Price, formerly of the Pratt Institute and the Rhode Island School of Design, contains dozens of useful suggestions for student and teacher alike. An indispensable teaching aid. Extensively revised. 16-page syllabus and 30 plates in slip cover, 16 x 22. T239 Clothbound **$6.00**

THE STYLES OF ORNAMENT, Alexander Speltz. Largest collection of ornaments in print— 3765 illustrations of prehistoric, Lombard, Gothic, Frank, Romanesque, Mohammedan, Renaissance, Polish, Swiss, Rococo, Sheraton, Empire, U. S. Colonial, etc., ornament. Gargoyles, dragons, columns, necklaces, urns, friezes, furniture, buildings, keyholes, tapestries, fantastic animals, armor, religious objects, much more, all in line. Reproduce any one free. Index. Bibliography. 400 plates. 656pp. 5⅝ x 8⅜. T557 Paperbound **$2.50**

HANDBOOK OF DESIGNS AND DEVICES, C. P. Hornung. This unique book is indispensable to the designer, commercial artist, and hobbyist. It is not a textbook but a working collection of 1836 basic designs and variations, carefully reproduced, which may be used without permission. Variations of circle, line, band, triangle, square, cross, diamond, swastika, pentagon, octagon, hexagon, star, scroll, interlacement, shields, etc. Supplementary notes on the background and symbolism of the figures. "A necessity to every designer who would be original without having to labor heavily," ARTIST AND ADVERTISER. 204 plates. 240pp. 5⅜ x 8. T125 Paperbound **$1.90**

THE UNIVERSAL PENMAN, George Bickham. This beautiful book, which first appeared in 1743, is the largest collection of calligraphic specimens, flourishes, alphabets, and calligraphic illustrations ever published. 212 full-page plates are drawn from the work of such 18th century masters of English roundhand as Dove, Champion, Bland, and 20 others. They contain 22 complete alphabets, over 2,000 flourishes, and 122 illustrations, each drawn with a stylistic grace impossible to describe. This book is invaluable to anyone interested in the beauties of calligraphy, or to any artist, hobbyist, or craftsman who wishes to use the very best ornamental handwriting and flourishes for decorative purposes. Commercial artists, advertising artists, have found it unexcelled as a source of material suggesting quality. "An essential part of any art library, and a book of permanent value," AMERICAN ARTIST. 212 plates. 224pp. 9 x 13¾. T20 Clothbound **$10.00**

1800 WOODCUTS BY THOMAS BEWICK AND HIS SCHOOL. Prepared by Dover's editorial staff, this is the largest collection of woodcuts by Bewick and his school ever compiled. Contains the complete engravings from all his major works and a wide range of illustrations from lesser-known collections, all photographed from clear copies of the original books and reproduced in line. Carefully and conveniently organized into sections on Nature (animals and birds, scenery and landscapes, plants, insects, etc.), People (love and courtship, social life, school and domestic scenes, misfortunes, costumes, etc.), Business and Trade, and illustrations from primers, fairytales, spelling books, frontispieces, borders, fables and allegories, etc. In addition to technical proficiency and simple beauty, Bewick's work is remarkable as a mode of pictorial symbolism, reflecting rustic tranquility, an atmosphere of rest, simplicity, idyllic contentment. A delight for the eye, an inexhaustible source of illustrative material for art studios, commercial artists, advertising agencies. Individual illustrations (up to 10 for any one use) are copyright free. Classified index. Bibliography and sources. Introduction by Robert Hutchinson. 1800 woodcuts. xiv + 247pp. 9 x 12. T766 Clothbound **$10.00**

A HANDBOOK OF EARLY ADVERTISING ART, C. P. Hornung. The largest collection of copyright-free early advertising art ever compiled. Vol. I contains some 2,000 illustrations of agricultural devices, animals, old automobiles, birds, buildings, Christmas decorations (with 7 Santa Clauses by Nast), allegorical figures, fire engines, horses and vehicles, Indians, portraits, sailing ships, trains, sports, trade cuts — and 30 other categories! Vol. II, devoted to typography, has over 4000 specimens: 600 different Roman, Gothic, Barnum, Old English faces; 630 ornamental type faces; 1115 initials, hundreds of scrolls, flourishes, etc. This third edition is enlarged by 78 additional plates containing all new material. "A remarkable collection," PRINTERS' INK. "A rich contribution to the history of American design," GRAPHIS. Volume I, Pictorial. Over 2000 illustrations. xiv + 242pp. 9 x 12. T122 Clothbound **$10.00** Volume II, Typographical. Over 4000 specimens. vii + 312pp. 9 x 12. T123 Clothbound **$10.00** Two volume set, T121 Clothbound, only **$18.50**

CATALOGUE OF DOVER BOOKS

DESIGN MOTIFS OF ANCIENT MEXICO, J. Enciso. This unique collection of pre-Columbian stamps for textiles and pottery contains 766 superb designs from Aztec, Olmec, Totonac, Maya, and Toltec origins. Plumed serpents, calendrical elements, wind gods, animals, flowers, demons, dancers, monsters, abstract ornament, and other designs. More than 90% of these illustrations are completely unobtainable elsewhere. Use this work to bring new barbaric beauty into your crafts or drawing. Originally $17.50. Printed in three colors. 766 illustrations, thousands of motifs. 192pp. 7⅞ x 10¾. **T84 Paperbound $1.85**

DECORATIVE ART OF THE SOUTHWEST INDIANS, D. S. Sides. A magnificent album of authentic designs (both pre- and post-Conquest) from the pottery, textiles, and basketry of the Navaho, Hopi, Mohave, Santo Domingo, and over 20 other Southwestern groups. Designs include birds, clouds, butterflies, quadrupeds, geometric forms, etc. A valuable book for folklorists, and a treasury for artists, designers, advertisers, and craftsmen, who may use without payment or permission any of the vigorous, colorful, and strongly rhythmic designs. Aesthetic and archeological notes. 50 plates. Bibliography of over 50 items. xviii + 101pp. 5⅝ x 8⅜. **T139 Paperbound $1.00**

PAINTING IN THE FAR EAST, Laurence Binyon. Excellent introduction by one of greatest authorities on subject studies 1500 years of oriental art (China, Japan; also Tibet, Persia), over 250 painters. Examines works, schools, influence of Wu Tao-tzu, Kanaoka, Toba Sojo, Masanobu, Okio, etc.; early traditions; Kamakura epoch; the Great Decorators; T'ang Dynasty; Matabei, beginnings of genre; Japanese woodcut, color print; much more, all chronological, in cultural context. 42 photos. Bibliography. 317pp. 6 x 9¼. **T520 Paperbound $2.00**

ON THE LAWS OF JAPANESE PAINTING, H. Bowie. This unusual book, based on 9 years of profound study-experience in the Late Kano art of Japan, remains the most authentic guide in English to the spirit and technique of Japanese painting. A wealth of interesting and useful data on control of the brush; practise exercises; manufacture of ink, brushes, colors; the use of various lines and dots to express moods. It is the best possible substitute for a series of lessons from a great oriental master. 66 plates with 220 illustrations. Index. xv + 177pp. 6⅛ x 9¼. **T30 Paperbound $1.95**

THE MATERIALS AND TECHNIQUES OF MEDIEVAL PAINTING, D. V. Thompson. Based on years of study of medieval manuscripts and laboratory analysis of medieval paintings, this book discusses carriers and grounds, binding media, pigments, metals used in painting, etc. Considers relative merits of painting al fresco and al secco, the procession of coloring materials, burnishing, and many other matters. Preface by Bernard Berenson. Index. 239pp. 5⅜ x 8. **T327 Paperbound $1.85**

THE CRAFTSMAN'S HANDBOOK, Cennino Cennini. This is considered the finest English translation of IL LIBRO DELL' ARTE, a 15th century Florentine introduction to art technique. It is both fascinating reading and a wonderful mirror of another culture for artists, art students, historians, social scientists, or anyone interested in details of life some 500 years ago. While it is not an exact recipe book, it gives directions for such matters as tinting papers, gilding stone, preparation of various hues of black, and many other useful but nearly forgotten facets of the painter's art. As a human document reflecting the ideas of a practising medieval artist it is particularly important. 4 illustrations. xxvii + 142pp. D. V. Thompson translator. 6⅛ x 9¼. **T54 Paperbound $1.35**

VASARI ON TECHNIQUE, G. Vasari. Pupil of Michelangelo and outstanding biographer of the Renaissance artists, Vasari also wrote this priceless treatise on the technical methods of the painters, architects, and sculptors of his day. This is the only English translation of this practical, informative, and highly readable work. Scholars, artists, and general readers will welcome these authentic discussions of marble statues, bronze casting, fresco painting, oil painting, engraving, stained glass, rustic fountains and grottoes, etc. Introduction and notes by G. B. Brown. Index. 18 plates, 11 figures. xxiv + 328pp. 5⅜ x 8. **T717 Paperbound $2.00**

METHODS AND MATERIALS OF PAINTING OF THE GREAT SCHOOLS AND MASTERS, C. L. Eastlake. A vast, complete, and authentic reconstruction of the secret techniques of the masters of painting, collected from hundreds of forgotten manuscripts by the eminent President of the British Royal Academy: Greek, Roman, and medieval techniques; fresco and tempera; varnishes and encaustics; the secrets of Leonardo, Van Eyck, Raphael, and many others. Art historians, students, teachers, critics, and laymen will gain new insights into the creation of the great masterpieces; while artists and craftsmen will have a treasury of valuable techniques. Index. Two volume set. Total of 1025pp. 5⅜ x 8. **T718 Paperbound $2.00**
T719 Paperbound $2.00
The set $4.00

BYZANTINE ART AND ARCHAEOLOGY, O. M. Dalton. Still the most thorough work in English—both in breadth and in depth—on the astounding multiplicity of Byzantine art forms throughout Europe, North Africa, and Western Asia from the 4th to the 15th century. Analyzes hundreds of individual pieces from over 160 public and private museums, libraries, and collections all over the world. Full treatment of Byzantine sculpture, painting, mosaic, jewelry, textiles, etc., including historical development, symbolism, and aesthetics. Chapters on iconography and ornament. Indispensable for study of Christian symbolism and medieval art. 457 illustrations, many full-page. Bibliography of over 2500 references. 4 Indexes. xx + 727pp. 6⅛ x 9¼. **T776 Clothbound $8.50**

CATALOGUE OF DOVER BOOKS

METALWORK AND ENAMELLING, H. Maryon. This is probably the best book ever written on the subject. Prepared by Herbert Maryon, F.S.A., of the British Museum, it tells everything necessary for home manufacture of jewelry, rings, ear pendants, bowls, and dozens of other objects. Clearly written chapters provide precise information on such topics as materials, tools, soldering, filigree, setting stones, raising patterns, spinning metal, repoussé work, hinges and joints, metal inlaying, damascening, overlaying, niello, Japanese alloys, enamelling, cloisonné, painted enamels, casting, polishing, coloring, assaying, and dozens of other techniques. This is the next best thing to apprenticeship to a master metalworker. 363 photographs and figures. 374pp. 5½ x 8½. **T183 Clothbound $8.50**

SILK SCREEN TECHNIQUES, J. I. Biegeleisen, Max A. Cohn. A complete-to-the-last-detail copiously illustrated home course in this fast growing modern art form. Full directions for building silk screen out of inexpensive materials; explanations of five basic methods of stencil preparation—paper, blockout, tusche, film, photographic—and effects possible: light and shade, washes, dry brush, oil paint type impastos, gouaches, pastels. Detailed coverage of multicolor printing, illustrated by proofs showing the stages of a 4 color print. Special section on common difficulties. 149 illustrations, 8 in color. Sources of supply. xiv + 187pp. 6⅛ x 9¼. **T433 Paperbound $1.55**

A HANDBOOK OF WEAVES, G. H. Oelsner. Now back in print! Probably the most complete book of weaves ever printed, fully explained, differentiated, and illustrated. Includes plain weaves; irregular, double-stitched, and filling satins; derivative, basket, and rib weaves; steep, undulating, broken, offset, corkscrew, interlocking, herringbone, and fancy twills; honeycomb, lace, and crepe weaves; tricot, matelassé, and montagnac weaves; and much more. Translated and revised by S. S. Dale, with supplement on the analysis of weaves and fabrics. 1875 illustrations. vii + 402pp. 6 x 9¼. **T209 Clothbound $5.00**

BASIC BOOKBINDING, A. W. Lewis. Enables the beginner and the expert to apply the latest and most simplified techniques to rebinding old favorites and binding new paperback books. Complete lists of all necessary materials and guides to the selection of proper tools, paper, glue, boards, cloth, leather, or sheepskin covering fabrics, lettering inks and pigments, etc. You are shown how to collate a book, sew it, back it, trim it, make boards and attach them in easy step-by-step stages. Author's preface. 261 illustrations with appendix. Index. xi + 144pp. 5⅜ x 8. **T169 Paperbound $1.35**

BASKETRY, F. J. Christopher. Basic introductions cover selection of materials, use and care of tools, equipment. Easy-to-follow instructions for preparation of oval, oblong trays, lidded baskets, rush mats, tumbler holders, bicycle baskets, waste paper baskets, many other useful, beautiful articles made of coiled and woven reed, willow, rushes, raffia. Special sections present in clear, simple language and numerous illustrations all the how-to information you could need: linings, skein wire, varieties of stitching, simplified construction of handles, dying processes. For beginner and skilled craftsman alike. Edited by Majorie O'Shaugnessy. Bibliography. Sources of supply. Index. 112 illustrations. 108pp. 5 x 7¼. **T903 Paperbound 75¢**

THE ART OF ETCHING, E. S. Lumsden. Everything you need to know to do etching yourself. First two sections devoted to technique of etching and engraving, covering such essentials as relative merits of zinc and copper, cleaning and grounding plates, gravers, acids, arrangement of etching-room, methods of biting, types of inks and oils, mounting, stretching and framing, preserving and restoring plates, size and color of printing papers, much more. A review of the history of the art includes separate chapters on Dürer and Lucas van Leyden, Rembrandt and Van Dyck, Goya, Meryon, Haden and Whistler, British masters of nineteenth century, modern etchers. Final section is a collection of prints by contemporary etchers with comments by the artists. Professional etchers and engravers will find this a highly useful source of examples. Beginners and teachers, students of art and printing will find it a valuable tool. Index. 208 illustrations. 384pp. 5⅜ x 8. **T49 Paperbound $2.50**

WHITTLING AND WOODCARVING, E. J. Tangerman. What to make and how to make it for even a moderately handy beginner. One of the few works that bridge gap between whittling and serious carving. History of the art, background information on selection and use of woods, grips, types of strokes and cuts, handling of tools and chapters on rustic work, flat toys and windmills, puzzles, chains, ships in bottle, nested spheres, fans, more than 100 useful, entertaining objects. Second half covers carving proper: woodcuts, low relief, sculpture in the round, lettering, inlay and marquetry, indoor and outdoor decorations, pierced designs, much more. Final chapter describes finishing, care of tools. Sixth edition. Index. 464 illustrations. x + 239pp. 5½ x 8⅛. **T965 Paperbound $1.75**

THE PRACTICE OF TEMPERA PAINTING, Daniel V. Thompson, Jr. A careful exposition of all aspects of tempera painting, including sections on many possible modern uses, propensities of various woods, choice of material for panel, making and applying the gesso, pigments and brushes, technique of the actual painting, gilding and so on—everything one need know to try a hand at this proven but neglected art. The author is unquestionably the world's leading authority on tempera methods and processes and his treatment is based on exhaustive study of manuscript material. Drawings and diagrams increase clarity of text. No one interested in tempera painting can afford to be without this book. Appendix, "Tempera Practice in Yale Art School," by Lewis E. York. 85 illustrations by York; 4 full-page plates. ix x 149pp. 5⅜ x 8½. **T343 Paperbound $1.50**

Teach Yourself

These British books are the most effective series of home study books on the market! With no outside help they will teach you as much as is necessary to have a good background in each subject, in many cases offering as much material as a similar high school or college course. They are carefully planned, written by foremost British educators, and amply provided with test questions and problems for you to check your progress; the mathematics books are especially rich in examples and problems. Do not confuse them with skimpy outlines or ordinary school texts or vague generalized popularizations; each book is complete in itself, full without being overdetailed, and designed to give you an easily-acquired branch of knowledge.

TEACH YOURSELF ALGEBRA, P. Abbott. The equivalent of a thorough high school course, up through logarithms. 52 illus. 307pp. 4¼ x 7.   T680 Clothbound **$2.00**

TEACH YOURSELF GEOMETRY, P. Abbott. Plane and solid geometry, covering about a year of plane and six months of solid. 268 illus. 344pp. 4½ x 7.   T681 Clothbound **$2.00**

TEACH YOURSELF TRIGONOMETRY, P. Abbott. Background of algebra and geometry will enable you to get equivalent of elementary college course. Tables. 102 illus. 204pp. 4½ x 7.
T682 Clothbound **$2.00**

TEACH YOURSELF THE CALCULUS, P. Abbott. With algebra and trigonometry you will be able to acquire a good working knowledge of elementary integral calculus and differential calculus. Excellent supplement to any course textbook. 380pp. 4¼ x 7.   T683 Clothbound **$2.00**

TEACH YOURSELF THE SLIDE RULE, B. Snodgrass. Basic principles clearly explained, with many applications in engineering, business, general figuring, will enable you to pick up very useful skill. 10 illus. 207pp. 4¼ x 7.   T684 Clothbound **$2.00**

TEACH YOURSELF MECHANICS, P. Abbott. Equivalent of part course on elementary college level, with lever, parallelogram of force, friction, laws of motion, gases, etc. Fine introduction before more advanced course. 163 illus. 271pp. 4½ x 7.   T685 Clothbound **$2.00**

TEACH YOURSELF ELECTRICITY, C. W. Wilman. Current, resistance, voltage, Ohm's law. circuits, generators, motors, transformers, etc. Non-mathematical as much as possible. 115 illus. 184pp. 4¼ x 7.   T230 Clothbound **$2.00**

TEACH YOURSELF HEAT ENGINES E. DeVille. Steam and internal combustion engines; nonmathematical introduction for student, for layman wishing background, refresher for advanced student. 76 illus. 217pp. 4¼ x 7.   T237 Clothbound **$2.00**

TEACH YOURSELF TO PLAY THE PIANO, King Palmer. Companion and supplement to lessons or self study. Handy reference, too. Nature of instrument, elementary musical theory, technique of playing, interpretation, etc. 60 illus. 144pp. 4¼ x 7.   T959 Clothbound **$2.00**

TEACH YOURSELF HERALDRY AND GENEALOGY, L. G. Pine. Modern work, avoiding romantic and overpopular misconceptions. Editor of new Burke presents detailed information and commentary down to present. Best general survey. 50 illus. glossary; 129pp. 4¼ x 7.
T962 Clothbound **$2.00**

TEACH YOURSELF HANDWRITING, John L. Dumpleton. Basic Chancery cursive style is popular and easy to learn. Many diagrams. 114 illus. 192pp. 4¼ x 7.   T960 Clothbound **$2.00**

TEACH YOURSELF CARD GAMES FOR TWO, Kenneth Konstam. Many first-rate games, including old favorites like cribbage and gin and canasta as well as new lesser-known games. Extremely interesting for cards enthusiast. 60 illus. 150pp. 4¼ x 7.   T963 Clothbound **$2.00**

TEACH YOURSELF GUIDEBOOK TO THE DRAMA, Luis Vargas. Clear, rapid survey of changing fashions and forms from Aeschylus to Tennessee Williams, in all major European traditions. Plot summaries, critical comments, etc. Equivalent of a college drama course; fine cultural background 224pp. 4¼ x 7.   T961 Clothbound **$2.00**

TEACH YOURSELF THE ORGAN, Francis Routh. Excellent compendium of background material for everyone interested in organ music, whether as listener or player. 27 musical illus. 158pp. 4¼ x 7.   T977 Clothbound **$2.00**

TEACH YOURSELF TO STUDY SCULPTURE, William Gaunt. Noted British cultural historian surveys culture from Greeks, primitive world, to moderns. Equivalent of college survey course. 23 figures, 40 photos. 158pp. 4¼ x 7.   T976 Clothbound **$2.00**

Miscellaneous

THE COMPLETE KANO JIU-JITSU (JUDO), H. I. Hancock and K. Higashi. Most comprehensive guide to judo, referred to as outstanding work by Encyclopaedia Britannica. Complete authentic Japanese system of 160 holds and throws, including the most spectacular, fully illustrated with 487 photos. Full text explains leverage, weight centers, pressure points, special tricks, etc.; shows how to protect yourself from almost any manner of attack though your attacker may have the initial advantage of strength and surprise. This authentic Kano system should not be confused with the many American imitations. xii + 500pp. 5⅜ x 8.
T639 Paperbound **$2.00**

THE MEMOIRS OF JACQUES CASANOVA. Splendid self-revelation by history's most engaging scoundrel—utterly dishonest with women and money, yet highly intelligent and observant. Here are all the famous duels, scandals, amours, banishments, thefts, treacheries, and imprisonments all over Europe: a life lived to the fullest and recounted with gusto in one of the greatest autobiographies of all time. What is more, these Memoirs are also one of the most trustworthy and valuable documents we have on the society and culture of the extravagant 18th century. Here are Voltaire, Louis XV, Catherine the Great, cardinals, castrati, pimps, and pawnbrokers—an entire glittering civilization unfolding before you with an unparalleled sense of actuality. Translated by Arthur Machen. Edited by F. A. Blossom. Introduction by Arthur Symons. Illustrated by Rockwell Kent. Total of xlviii + 2216pp. 5⅜ x 8.
T338 Vol I   Paperbound **$2.00**
T339 Vol II Paperbound **$2.00**
T340 Vol III Paperbound **$2.00**
The set **$6.00**

BARNUM'S OWN STORY, P. T. Barnum. The astonishingly frank and gratifyingly well-written autobiography of the master showman and pioneer publicity man reveals the truth about his early career, his famous hoaxes (such as the Fejee Mermaid and the Woolly Horse), his amazing commercial ventures, his fling in politics, his feuds and friendships, his failures and surprising comebacks. A vast panorama of 19th century America's mores, amusements, and vitality. 66 new illustrations in this edition. xii + 500pp. 5⅜ x 8.
T764 Paperbound **$1.65**

THE STORY OF THE TITANIC AS TOLD BY ITS SURVIVORS, ed. by Jack Winocour. Most significant accounts of most overpowering naval disaster of modern times: all 4 authors were survivors. Includes 2 full-length, unabridged books: "The Loss of the S.S. Titanic," by Laurence Beesley, "The Truth about the Titanic," by Col. Archibald Gracie, 6 pertinent chapters from "Titanic and Other Ships," autobiography of only officer to survive, Second Officer Charles Lightoller; and a short, dramatic account by the Titanic's wireless operator, Harold Bride. 26 illus. 368pp. 5⅜ x 8.
T610 Paperbound **$1.50**

THE PHYSIOLOGY OF TASTE, Jean Anthelme Brillat-Savarin. Humorous, satirical, witty, and personal classic on joys of food and drink by 18th century French politician, litterateur. Treats the science of gastronomy, erotic value of truffles, Parisian restaurants, drinking contests; gives recipes for tunny omelette, pheasant, Swiss fondue, etc. Only modern translation of original French edition. Introduction. 41 illus. 346pp. 5⅜ x 8⅜.
T591 Paperbound **$1.50**

THE ART OF THE STORY-TELLER, M. L. Shedlock. This classic in the field of effective story-telling is regarded by librarians, story-tellers, and educators as the finest and most lucid book on the subject. The author considers the nature of the story, the difficulties of communicating stories to children, the artifices used in story-telling, how to obtain and maintain the effect of the story, and, of extreme importance, the elements to seek and those to avoid in selecting material. A 99-page selection of Miss Shedlock's most effective stories and an extensive bibliography of further material by Eulalie Steinmetz enhance the book's usefulness. xxi + 320pp. 5⅜ x 8.
T635 Paperbound **$1.50**

CREATIVE POWER: THE EDUCATION OF YOUTH IN THE CREATIVE ARTS, Hughes Mearns. In first printing considered revolutionary in its dynamic, progressive approach to teaching the creative arts; now accepted as one of the most effective and valuable approaches yet formulated. Based on the belief that every child has something to contribute, it provides in a stimulating manner invaluable and inspired teaching insights, to stimulate children's latent powers of creative expression in drama, poetry, music, writing, etc. Mearns's methods were developed in his famous experimental classes in creative education at the Lincoln School of Teachers College, Columbia Univ. Named one of the 20 foremost books on education in recent times by National Education Association. New enlarged revised 2nd edition. Introduction. 272pp. 5⅜ x 8.
T490 Paperbound **$1.75**

FREE AND INEXPENSIVE EDUCATIONAL AIDS, T. J. Pepe, Superintendent of Schools, Southbury, Connecticut. An up-to-date listing of over 1500 booklets, films, charts, etc. 5% costs less than 25¢; 1% costs more; 94% is yours for the asking. Use this material privately, or in schools from elementary to college, for discussion, vocational guidance, projects. 59 categories include health, trucking, textiles, language, weather, the blood, office practice, wild life, atomic energy, other important topics. Each item described according to contents, number of pages or running time, level. All material is educationally sound, and without political or company bias. 1st publication. Second, revised edition. Index. 244pp. 5⅜ x 8.
T663 Paperbound **$1.50**

CATALOGUE OF DOVER BOOKS

THE ROMANCE OF WORDS, E. Weekley. An entertaining collection of unusual word-histories that tracks down for the general reader the origins of more than 2000 common words and phrases in English (including British and American slang): discoveries often surprising, often humorous, that help trace vast chains of commerce in products and ideas. There are Arabic trade words, cowboy words, origins of family names, phonetic accidents, curious wanderings, folk-etymologies, etc. Index. xiii + 210pp. 5⅜ x 8. T710 Paperbound **$1.25**

PHRASE AND WORD ORIGINS: A STUDY OF FAMILIAR EXPRESSIONS, A. H. Holt. One of the most entertaining books on the unexpected origins and colorful histories of words and phrases, based on sound scholarship, but written primarily for the layman. Over 1200 phrases and 1000 separate words are covered, with many quotations, and the results of the most modern linguistic and historical researches. "A right jolly book Mr. Holt has made," N. Y. Times. v + 254pp. 5⅜ x 8. T758 Paperbound **$1.35**

AMATEUR WINE MAKING, S. M. Tritton. Now, with only modest equipment and no prior knowledge, you can make your own fine table wines. A practical handbook, this covers every type of grape wine, as well as fruit, flower, herb, vegetable, and cereal wines, and many kinds of mead, cider, and beer. Every question you might have is answered, and there is a valuable discussion of what can go wrong at various stages along the way. Special supplement of yeasts and American sources of supply. 13 tables. 32 illustrations. Glossary. Index. 239pp. 5½ x 8½. T514 Clothbound **$4.00**

SAILING ALONE AROUND THE WORLD. Captain Joshua Slocum. A great modern classic in a convenient inexpensive edition. Captain Slocum's account of his single-handed voyage around the world in a 34 foot boat which he rebuilt himself. A nearly unparalleled feat of seamanship told with vigor, wit, imagination, and great descriptive power. "A nautical equivalent of Thoreau's account," Van Wyck Brooks. 67 illustrations. 308pp. 5⅜ x 8. T326 Paperbound **$1.00**

FARES, PLEASE! by J. A. Miller. Authoritative, comprehensive, and entertaining history of local public transit from its inception to its most recent developments: trolleys, horsecars, streetcars, buses, elevateds, subways, along with monorails, "road-railers," and a host of other extraordinary vehicles. Here are all the flamboyant personalities involved, the vehement arguments, the unusual information, and all the nostalgia. "Interesting facts brought into especially vivid life," N. Y. Times. New preface. 152 illustrations, 4 new. Bibliography. xix + 204pp. 5⅜ x 8. T671 Paperbound **$1.50**

HOAXES, C. D. MacDougall. Shows how art, science, history, journalism can be perverted for private purposes. Hours of delightful entertainment and a work of scholarly value, this often shocking book tells of the deliberate creation of nonsense news, the Cardiff giant, Shakespeare forgeries, the Loch Ness monster, Biblical frauds, political schemes, literary hoaxers like Chatterton, Ossian, the disumbrationist school of painting, the lady in black at Valentino's tomb, and over 250 others. It will probably reveal the truth about a few things you've believed, and help you spot more readily the editorial "gander" and planted publicity release. "A stupendous collection . . . and shrewd analysis." New Yorker. New revised edition. 54 photographs. Index. 320pp. 5⅜ x 8. T465 Paperbound **$1.75**

A HISTORY OF THE WARFARE OF SCIENCE WITH THEOLOGY IN CHRISTENDOM, A. D. White. Most thorough account ever written of the great religious-scientific battles shows gradual victory of science over ignorant, harmful beliefs. Attacks on theory of evolution; attacks on Galileo; great medieval plagues caused by belief in devil-origin of disease; attacks on Franklin's experiments with electricity; the witches of Salem; scores more that will amaze you. Author, co-founder and first president of Cornell U., writes with vast scholarly background, but in clear, readable prose. Acclaimed as classic effort in America to do away with superstition. Index. Total of 928pp. 5⅜ x 8. T608 Vol I Paperbound **$1.85** / T609 Vol II Paperbound **$1.85**

THE SHIP OF FOOLS, Sebastian Brant. First printed in 1494 in Basel, this amusing book swept Europe, was translated into almost every important language, and was a best-seller for centuries. That it is still living and vital is shown by recent developments in publishing. This is the only English translation of this work, and it recaptures in lively, modern verse all the wit and insights of the original, in satirizations of foibles and vices: greed, adultery, envy, hatred, sloth, profiteering, etc. This will long remain the definitive English edition, for Professor Zeydel has provided biography of Brant, bibliography, publishing history, influences, etc. Complete reprint of 1944 edition. Translated by Professor E. Zeydel, University of Cincinnati. All 114 original woodcut illustrations. viii + 399pp. 5½ x 8⅝. T266 Paperbound **$2.00**

ERASMUS, A STUDY OF HIS LIFE, IDEALS AND PLACE IN HISTORY, Preserved Smith. This is the standard English biography and evaluation of the great Netherlands humanist Desiderius Erasmus. Written by one of the foremost American historians it covers all aspects of Erasmus's life, his influence in the religious quarrels of the Reformation, his overwhelming role in the field of letters, and his importance in the emergence of the new world view of the Northern Renaissance. This is not only a work of great scholarship, it is also an extremely interesting, vital portrait of a great man. 8 illustrations. xiv + 479pp. 5⅝ x 8½. T331 Paperbound **$2.00**

Dover Classical Records

Now available directly to the public exclusively from Dover: top-quality recordings of fine classical music for only $2 per record! Originally released by a major company (except for the previously unreleased Gimpel recording of Bach) to sell for $5 and $6, these records were issued under our imprint only after they had passed a severe critical test. We insisted upon:

First-rate music that is enjoyable, musically important and culturally significant.

First-rate performances, where the artists have carried out the composer's intentions, in which the music is alive, vigorous, played with understanding and sympathy.

First-rate sound—clear, sonorous, fully balanced, crackle-free, whir-free.

Have in your home music by major composers, performed by such gifted musicians as Elsner, Gitlis, Wührer, the Barchet Quartet, Gimpel. Enthusiastically received when first released, many of these performances are definitive. The records are not seconds or remainders, but brand new pressings made on pure vinyl from carefully chosen master tapes. "All purpose" 12" monaural 33⅓ rpm records, they play equally well on hi-fi and stereo equipment. Fine music for discriminating music lovers, superlatively played, flawlessly recorded: there is no better way to build your library of recorded classical music at remarkable savings. There are no strings; this is not a come-on, not a club, forcing you to buy records you may not want in order to get a few at a lower price. Buy whatever records you want in any quantity, and never pay more than $2 each. Your obligation ends with your first purchase. And that's when ours begins. Dover's money-back guarantee allows you to return any record for any reason, even if you don't like the music, for a full, immediate refund, no questions asked.

MOZART: STRING QUARTET IN A MAJOR (K.464); STRING QUARTET IN C MAJOR ("DISSONANT", K.465), Barchet Quartet. The final two of the famed Haydn Quartets, high-points in the history of music. The A Major was accepted with delight by Mozart's contemporaries, but the C Major, with its dissonant opening, aroused strong protest. Today, of course, the remarkable resolutions of the dissonances are recognized as major musical achievements. "Beautiful warm playing," MUSICAL AMERICA. "Two of Mozart's loveliest quartets in a distinguished performance," REV. OF RECORDED MUSIC. (Playing time 58 mins.) HCR 5200 **$2.00**

MOZART: QUARTETS IN G MAJOR (K.80); D MAJOR (K.155); G MAJOR (K.156); C MAJOR (K157), Barchet Quartet. The early chamber music of Mozart receives unfortunately little attention. First-rate music of the Italian school, it contains all the lightness and charm that belongs only to the youthful Mozart. This is currently the only separate source for the composer's work of this time period. "Excellent," HIGH FIDELITY. "Filled with sunshine and youthful joy; played with verve, recorded sound live and brilliant," CHRISTIAN SCI. MONITOR. (Playing time 51 mins.) HCR 5201 **$2.00**

MOZART: SERENADE #9 IN D MAJOR ("POSTHORN", K.320); SERENADE #6 IN D MAJOR ("SERENATA NOTTURNA", K.239), Pro Musica Orch. of Stuttgart, under Edouard van Remoortel. For Mozart, the serenade was a highly effective form, since he could bring to it the immediacy and intimacy of chamber music as well as the free fantasy of larger group music. Both these serenades are distinguished by a playful, mischievous quality, a spirit perfectly captured in this fine performance. "A triumph, polished playing from the orchestra," HI FI MUSIC AT HOME. "Sound is rich and resonant, fidelity is wonderful," REV. OF RECORDED MUSIC. (Playing time 51 mins.) HCR 5202 **$2.00**

MOZART: DIVERTIMENTO IN E FLAT MAJOR FOR STRING TRIO (K.563); ADAGIO AND FUGUE IN F MINOR FOR STRING TRIO (K.404a), Kehr Trio. The Divertimento is one of Mozart's most beloved pieces, called by Einstein "the finest, most perfect trio ever heard." It is difficult to imagine a music lover who will not be delighted by it. This is the only recording of the lesser known Adagio and Fugue, written in 1782 and influenced by Bach's Well-Tempered Clavichord. "Extremely beautiful recording, strongly recommended," THE OBSERVER. "Superior to rival editions," HIGH FIDELITY. (Playing time 51 mins.) HCR 5203 **$2.00**

SCHUMANN: KREISLERIANA (OP.16); FANTASY IN C MAJOR ("FANTASIE," OP.17), Vlado Perlemuter, Piano. The vigorous Romantic imagination and the remarkable emotional qualities of Schumann's piano music raise it to special eminence in 19th century creativity. Both these pieces are rooted to the composer's tortuous romance with his future wife, Clara, and both receive brilliant treatment at the hands of Vlado Perlemuter, Paris Conservatory, proclaimed by Alfred Cortot "not only a great virtuoso but also a great musician." "The best Kreisleriana to date," BILLBOARD. (Playing time 55 mins.) HCR 5204 **$2.00**

SCHUMANN: TRIO #1, D MINOR; TRIO #3, G MINOR, Trio di Bolzano. The fiery, romantic, melodic Trio #1, and the dramatic, seldom heard Trio #3 are both movingly played by a fine chamber ensemble. No one personified Romanticism to the general public of the 1840's more than did Robert Schumann, and among his most romantic works are these trios for cello, violin and piano. "Ensemble and overall interpretation leave little to be desired," HIGH FIDELITY. "An especially understanding performance," REV. OF RECORDED MUSIC. (Playing time 54 mins.) HCR 5205 **$2.00**

New Books

101 PATCHWORK PATTERNS, Ruby Short McKim. With no more ability than the fundamentals of ordinary sewing, you will learn to make over 100 beautiful quilts: flowers, rainbows, Irish chains, fish and bird designs, leaf designs, unusual geometric patterns, many others. Cutting designs carefully diagrammed and described, suggestions for materials, yardage estimates, step-by-step instructions, plus entertaining stories of origins of quilt names, other folklore. Revised 1962. 101 full-sized patterns. 140 illustrations. Index. 128pp. 7⅞ x 10¾.
T773 Paperbound **$1.85**

ESSENTIAL GRAMMAR SERIES
By concentrating on the essential core of material that constitutes the semantically most important forms and areas of a language and by stressing explanation (often bringing parallel English forms into the discussion) rather than rote memory, this new series of grammar books is among the handiest language aids ever devised. Designed by linguists and teachers for adults with limited learning objectives and learning time, these books omit nothing important, yet they teach more usable language material and do it more quickly and permanently than any other self-study material. Clear and rigidly economical, they concentrate upon immediately usable language material, logically organized so that related material is always presented together. Any reader of typical capability can use them to refresh his grasp of language, to supplement self-study language records or conventional grammars used in schools, or to begin language study on his own. Now available:

ESSENTIAL GERMAN GRAMMAR, Dr. Guy Stern & E. F. Bleiler. Index. Glossary of terms. 128pp. 4½ x 6⅜.
T422 Paperbound **75¢**

ESSENTIAL FRENCH GRAMMAR, Dr. Seymour Resnick. Index. Cognate list. Glossary. 159pp. 4½ x 6⅜.
T419 Paperbound **75¢**

ESSENTIAL ITALIAN GRAMMAR, Dr. Olga Ragusa. Index. Glossary. 111pp. 4½ x 6⅜.
T779 Paperbound **75¢**

ESSENTIAL SPANISH GRAMMAR, Dr. Seymour Resnick. Index. 50-page cognate list. Glossary. 138pp. 4½ x 6⅜.
T780 Paperbound **75¢**

PHILOSOPHIES OF MUSIC HISTORY: A Study of General Histories of Music, 1600-1960, Warren D. Allen. Unquestionably one of the most significant documents yet to appear in musicology, this thorough survey covers the entire field of historical research in music. An influential masterpiece of scholarship, it includes early music histories; theories on the ethos of music; lexicons, dictionaries and encyclopedias of music; musical historiography through the centuries; philosophies of music history; scores of related topics. Copiously documented. New preface brings work up to 1960. Index. 317-item bibliography. 9 illustrations; 3 full-page plates. 5⅜ x 8½. xxxiv + 382pp.
T282 Paperbound **$2.00**

MR. DOOLEY ON IVRYTHING AND IVRYBODY, Finley Peter Dunne. The largest collection in print of hilarious utterances by the irrepressible Irishman of Archey Street, one of the most vital characters in American fiction. Gathered from the half dozen books that appeared during the height of Mr. Dooley's popularity, these 102 pieces are all unaltered and uncut, and they are all remarkably fresh and pertinent even today. Selected and edited by Robert Hutchinson. 5⅜ x 8½. xii + 244p.
T626 Paperbound **$1.00**

TREATISE ON PHYSIOLOGICAL OPTICS, Hermann von Helmholtz. Despite new investigations, this important work will probably remain preeminent. Contains everything known about physiological optics up to 1925, covering scores of topics of dioptrics of the eye, sensations of vision, and perceptions of vision. Von Helmholtz's voluminous data are all included, as are extensive supplementary matter incorporated into the third German edition, new material prepared for 1925 English edition, and copious textual annotations by J. P. C. Southall. The most exhaustive treatise ever prepared on the subject, it has behind it a list of contributors that will never again be duplicated. Translated and edited by J. P. C. Southall. Bibliography. Indexes. 312 illustrations. 3 volumes bound as 2. Total of 1749pp. 5⅜ x 8.
S15-16 Two volume set, Clothbound **$15.00**

THE ARTISTIC ANATOMY OF TREES, Rex Vicat Cole. Even the novice with but an elementary knowledge of drawing and none of the structure of trees can learn to draw, paint trees from this systematic, lucid instruction book. Copiously illustrated with the author's own sketches, diagrams, and 50 paintings from the early Renaissance to today, it covers composition; structure of twigs, boughs, buds, branch systems; outline forms of major species; how leaf is set on twig; flowers and fruit and their arrangement; etc. 500 illustrations. Bibliography. Indexes. 347pp. 5⅜ x 8.
T1016 Clothbound **$4.50**

CATALOGUE OF DOVER BOOKS

GEOMETRY OF FOUR DIMENSIONS, H. P. Manning. Unique in English as a clear, concise introduction to this fascinating subject. Treatment is primarily synthetic and Euclidean, although hyperplanes and hyperspheres at infinity are considered by non-Euclidean forms. Historical introduction and foundations of 4-dimensional geometry; perpendicularity; simple angles; angles of planes; higher order; symmetry; order, motion; hyperpyramids, hypercones, hyperspheres; figures with parallel elements; volume, hypervolume in space; regular polyhedroids. Glossary of terms. 74 illustrations. ix + 348pp. 5⅜ x 8. S182 Paperbound **$2.00**

PAPER FOLDING FOR BEGINNERS, W. D. Murray and F. J. Rigney. A delightful introduction to the varied and entertaining Japanese art of origami (paper folding), with a full, crystal-clear text that anticipates every difficulty; over 275 clearly labeled diagrams of all important stages in creation. You get results at each stage, since complex figures are logically developed from simpler ones. 43 different pieces are explained: sailboats, frogs, roosters, etc. 6 photographic plates. 279 diagrams. 95pp. 5⅝ x 8⅜. T713 Paperbound **$1.00**

SATELLITES AND SCIENTIFIC RESEARCH, D. King-Hele. An up-to-the-minute non-technical account of the man-made satellites and the discoveries they have yielded up to September of 1961. Brings together information hitherto published only in hard-to-get scientific journals. Includes the life history of a typical satellite, methods of tracking, new information on the shape of the earth, zones of radiation, etc. Over 60 diagrams and 6 photographs. Mathematical appendix. Bibliography of over 100 items. Index. xii + 180pp. 5⅜ x 8½. T703 Paperbound **$2.00**

LOUIS PASTEUR, S. J. Holmes. A brief, very clear, and warmly understanding biography of the great French scientist by a former Professor of Zoology in the University of California. Traces his home life, the fortunate effects of his education, his early researches and first theses, and his constant struggle with superstition and institutionalism in his work on microorganisms, fermentation, anthrax, rabies, etc. New preface by the author. 159pp. 5⅜ x 8. T197 Paperbound **$1.00**

THE ENJOYMENT OF CHESS PROBLEMS, K. S. Howard. A classic treatise on this minor art by an internationally recognized authority that gives a basic knowledge of terms and themes for the everyday chess player as well as the problem fan: 7 chapters on the two-mover; 7 more on 3- and 4-move problems; a chapter on selfmates; and much more. "The most important one-volume contribution originating solely in the U.S.A.," Alain White. 200 diagrams. Index. Solutions, viii + 212pp. 5⅜ x 8. T742 Paperbound **$1.25**

SAM LOYD AND HIS CHESS PROBLEMS, Alain C. White. Loyd was (for all practical purposes) the father of the American chess problem and his protégé and successor presents here the diamonds of his production, chess problems embodying a whimsy and bizarre fancy entirely unique. More than 725 in all, ranging from two-move to extremely elaborate five-movers, including Loyd's contributions to chess oddities—problems in which pieces are arranged to form initials, figures, other by-paths of chess problem found nowhere else. Classified according to major concept, with full text analyzing problems, containing selections from Loyd's own writings. A classic to challenge your ingenuity, increase your skill. Corrected republication of 1913 edition. Over 750 diagrams and illustrations. 744 problems with solutions. 471pp. 5⅜ x 8½. T928 Paperbound **$2.00**

FABLES IN SLANG & MORE FABLES IN SLANG, George Ade. 2 complete books of major American humorist in pungent colloquial tradition of Twain, Billings. 1st reprinting in over 30 years includes "The Two Mandolin Players and the Willing Performer," "The Base Ball Fan Who Took the Only Known Cure," "The Slim Girl Who Tried to Keep a Date that was Never Made," 42 other tales of eccentric, perverse, but always funny characters. "Touch of genius," H. L. Mencken. New introduction by E. F. Bleiler. 86 illus. 208pp. 5⅜ x 8. T533 Paperbound **$1.00**

Prices subject to change without notice.

Dover publishes books on art, music, philosophy, literature, languages, history, social sciences, psychology, handcrafts, orientalia, puzzles and entertainments, chess, pets and gardens, books explaining science, intermediate and higher mathematics, mathematical physics, engineering, biological sciences, earth sciences, classics of science, etc. Write to:

Dept. catrr.
Dover Publications, Inc.
180 Varick Street, N. Y. 14, N. Y.

13 201